THE
WARRIORS
GUIDE

WARRIORS

THE NEW PROPHECY

POWER OF THREE

OMEN OF THE STARS

EXPLORE THE
WARRIORS
WORLD

Also by Erin Hunter

SEEKERS

Book One: The Quest Begins
Book Two: Great Bear Lake
Book Three: Smoke Mountain
Book Four: The Last Wilderness
Book Five: Fire in the Sky
Book Six: Spirits in the Stars

RETURN TO THE WILD
Book One: Island of Shadows
Book Two: The Melting Sea

MANGA
Toklo's Story
Kallik's Adventure

SURVIVORS

Book One: The Empty City

THE
WARRIORS
GUIDE

ERIN HUNTER

HARPER
An Imprint of HarperCollinsPublishers

The Warriors Guide

Copyright © 2012 by Working Partners Limited

Illustrations © 2007, 2009, 2010 Wayne McLoughlin

Warriors Adventure Game © Working Partners Limited

ISBN 978-0-06-206235-2

12 13 14 15 16 RRDH 10 9 8 7 6 5 4 3 2 1
❖
First Edition

CONTENTS

THUNDER, WIND, RIVER, SHADOW, AND STAR:

THE CLANS

The story of the beginning of the warrior Clans
has been passed down by cats of all Clans, from elder to warrior,
from warrior to apprentice, from queen to kit. The story
is never the same twice, and parts grow uncertain,
or they become suddenly clear in the telling. There are some cats
who walk dimly, their names and deeds lost in the sweet fog
of the elders' den, for the warrior Clans have roamed
the forest for moons beyond counting. . . .

THE DAWN
OF THE CLANS

Many moons ago, a community of cats settled in dense woodland close to the edge of a moor. Some were kittypets intrigued by the idea of exploring beyond their housefolk's backyard; others had been born and raised in the wild, by cats who knew how to catch their own prey and find shelter in the cold nights of leaf-bare.

The woodland, with the river running fast and deep at the edge of the trees, proved to be good territory for the cats. There was enough shelter for every cat, enough prey to feed them all, and the freedom to hunt among the trees, on the open moor, and along the fish-filled river.

The cats began to settle according to their preferences for hunting and prey. The fish-eaters kept mostly to the banks of the river, making their dens among the reeds and twisted willow roots; the mouse-pouncers stayed under the densest trees, perfecting their leaps among the tangled undergrowth; the rabbit-chasers, faster and leaner than the other cats, kept to the open moor; the squirrel-stalkers settled in the sparser woodland, where they learned to climb trees and hunt among the branches; and the cats who had a taste for snakes and lizards, and the cunning to catch them on marshy ground, settled among brittle grass stalks and rattling pine trees on the farthest edge of the territory.

There were no borders at first, and within each hunting ground the cats lived separately, meeting only as they went in pursuit of the same prey. Occasionally cats clashed over a piece of fresh-kill or a good place for a den, but battles between large numbers of cats were unheard of.

Then a time came when prey was scarce, and there were too many mouths to feed and bodies to shelter in each hunting ground. Battles broke out, just a few cats at first, but more and more until hunting ground took on hunting ground, fighting for survival, not just for themselves, but for the cats who lived alongside them. After one dreadful battle, when the ground beneath the four great oak trees turned red with blood, the spirits of the dead cats came back to plead for peace with the strongest cats from each hunting ground: Wind, River, Thunder, Shadow, and Sky.

The five vowed to their fallen companions that they would find a way to put an end to the fighting, to live in their separate hunting grounds in communities that would preserve each territory for generations of cats to come.

THE TIME OF THE
CLANS HAD BEGUN...

THE WARRIOR CODE

1. Defend your Clan, even with your life. You may have friendships with cats from other Clans, but your loyalty must remain to your Clan, as one day you may meet them in battle.
2. Do not hunt or trespass on another Clan's territory.
3. Elders and kits must be fed before apprentices and warriors. Unless they have permission, apprentices may not eat until they have hunted to feed the elders.
4. Prey is killed only to be eaten. Give thanks to StarClan for its life.
5. A kit must be at least six moons old to become an apprentice.
6. Newly appointed warriors will keep a silent vigil for one night after receiving their warrior name.
7. A cat cannot be made deputy without having mentored at least one apprentice.
8. The deputy will become Clan leader when the leader dies or retires.

9. After the death or retirement of the deputy, the new deputy must be chosen before moonhigh.

10. A gathering of all four Clans is held at the full moon during a truce that lasts for the night. There shall be no fighting among Clans at this time.

11. Boundaries must be checked and marked daily. Challenge all trespassing cats.

12. No warrior may neglect a kit in pain or in danger, even if that kit is from a different Clan.

13. The word of the Clan leader is the warrior code.

14. An honorable warrior does not need to kill other cats to win his battles, unless they are outside the warrior code or it is necessary for self-defense.

15. A warrior rejects the soft life of a kittypet.

ThunderClan

THUNDERCLAN FACTS

Leader: Firestar
Deputy: Brambleclaw
Medicine cat: Jayfeather
Hunting territory: Forest
Camp: Stone hollow
Unique battle skill: Fighting in dense undergrowth

Clan character: In peace, respectful of other Clans. In battle, fierce, courageous, and loyal. ThunderClan cats speak out for what is right and are not afraid to challenge the warrior code.

Prey: Mice, voles, squirrels, the occasional rabbit, and birds such as starlings, magpies, wood pigeons, and thrushes.

Hunting skills: Excellent stalking techniques. They keep upwind of their prey, creeping across the forest floor unseen and unheard.

SIGNIFICANT LEADERS

Only some leaders and medicine cats are remembered by the Clans. Their names cast long shadows over the history of the forest; their deeds—good or evil—are told and retold by each generation until they pass from history into legend. Of the others, the ones whose names and deeds have been forgotten or, in some cases, banished from living memory, only StarClan knows.

THUNDERSTAR

Large orange tom the color of autumn leaves, with amber eyes and big white paws.

Strong, courageous, and determined.

Founder of ThunderClan—worked with Wind, Shadow, and River to develop the warrior code. According to legend it was Thunderstar who insisted on its more compassionate elements.

Deputies: Lightningtail, Owleyes (later Owlstar)

Apprentices: Unknown

OWLSTAR

Dark gray cat with large, unblinking amber eyes.

ThunderClan's second leader was a legendary hunter, who learned the ways of the tawny owl to stalk prey by night in silence.

Deputies: Unknown
Apprentices: Unknown

SUNSTAR

Tom with yellow tabby stripes, green eyes, and long fur.
Fair minded, even tempered, wise.
Held his Clan together through dangerous leaf-bare.
Fought to keep Sunningrocks away from RiverClan.
Deputies: Tawnyspots, Bluefur (later Bluestar)
Apprentice: Lionpaw (Lionheart)

BLUESTAR

Blue-gray she-cat with piercing blue eyes and silver hairs
   tipping muzzle and tail.
Wise, kind, beloved, and strong.
Brought a kittypet named Rusty to join ThunderClan. Rusty
   (renamed Firepaw, and later Fireheart) grew to become one
   of the most essential, valued, and respected cats in all the
   forest.
Deputies: Redtail, Lionheart, Tigerclaw, Fireheart (later Firestar)
Apprentices: Frostpaw (Frostfur), Runningpaw (Runningwind),
   Firepaw (Fireheart)

FIRESTAR

Tom with bright green eyes and flame-colored pelt.
Brave, intelligent, loyal—a natural leader.
Has an unusually strong connection with StarClan, and is the
   subject of StarClan's prophecy, "Fire alone can save our
   Clan".

Brought WindClan back from exile after they were driven out
by ShadowClan.

Uncovered Tigerclaw's treachery in time to stop him from
killing Bluestar.

Saved Clan from terrible fire in camp.

Discovered Tigerstar's scheme to unleash a pack of dogs to the
camp, and organized plan to save Clan.

Led the Clans of the forest against BloodClan.

Kept Clan together through the Twoleg destruction and brought
them safely to new lake home.

Deputies: Whitestorm, Graystripe, Brambleclaw

Apprentices: Cinderpaw (Cinderpelt), Cloudpaw (Cloudtail),
Brramblepaw (Brambleclaw)

SIGNIFICANT MEDICINE CATS

CLOUDSPOTS

Long-furred black tom with white ears, white chest, and two
white paws.

Inquiring, curious, and thoughtful, though sometimes appeared
shy and reserved.

Very interested in the theory of medicine—not quite so keen on
dealing with sickly kits.

Discovered the difference between greencough and whitecough, and identified catnip as a possible cure.

FEATHERWHISKER

Pale, silvery gray tom with bright amber eyes, unusually long
feathery whiskers, and a sweeping plume of a tail.

Sunstar's medicine cat and also his brother.

Gentle, sweet-natured, and kind mentor—passed on his com-
passion and deep connection with StarClan to his
apprentice, Spottedleaf.

Worked tirelessly to save Clanmates during greencough epidemic, which ultimately killed him.

SPOTTEDLEAF

Beautiful dark tortoiseshell she-cat with amber eyes, white
paws, black-tipped tail, and distinctive dappled coat.

Skilled interpreter of StarClan's mysterious messages.

Received StarClan prophecy that led Bluestar to bring Firepaw
into Clan.

Walks in dreams of ThunderClan cats, especially Firestar's.

YELLOWFANG

Ornery gray she-cat with bright orange eyes and broad,
flattened face.

Gifted healer—could be bad-tempered and difficult.

Helped rescue ThunderClan kits from ShadowClan.

Became ThunderClan's medicine cat after Spottedleaf was killed.

Died as lived—fighting to save Clan.

CINDERPELT

Fluffy gray she-cat with enormous blue eyes.

Bright and energetic with boundless enthusiasm.

Quick learner—could have been agile warrior, were it not for injury.

Rescued two ShadowClan cats and nursed them back to health against orders.

Nursed Bluestar back to health when she contracted greencough.

Saved Brightpaw's life after the apprentice was mauled by the pack of dogs.

Died fighting to save Sorreltail.

LEAFPOOL

Small, light brown tabby with amber eyes, white paws, and white chest.

Quiet and soft-spoken—the opposite of her sister Squirrelflight!

Through their deep connection, she and her sister are able to share each other's feelings and dreams.

Found Moonpool—the place in Clans' new lake home where they can communicate with StarClan.

Saved RiverClan from deadly Twoleg poison by helping Hawkfrost, and helped Mothwing cure the cats.

Nursed Clan back to health after badger attack.

According to StarClan, Leafpool faces a destiny unlike any medicine cat before her.

Forest Attack: How ThunderClan Keeps the Element of Surprise

1. Move quietly and communicate with signals. Cracking twigs, startled birds, and rustling bracken will tell the enemy exactly where you are.

2. Keep downwind of the trespassers so that your scent doesn't give you away.

3. Look for freshly broken twigs, overturned leaves on the forest floor, remains of prey, or a clump of fur caught on a bramble. Any animal that moves through the forest leaves behind signs that it's passed by—and signs like this could lead you straight to the invaders.

4. Keep your mouth open to search for unfamiliar scents. Be careful: If there is scent when there is no breeze to carry it through the forest, it could mean that your enemy is very close by.

5. Light-colored pelts are easily seen against brown and green foliage, so stay in the thickest cover. Keep low—the enemy will be looking for movement at normal head height, not close to the ground.

6. Never miss an opportunity to perfect your tracking ability. In the nursery, kits sneak up on their mothers and pounce with their moss-soft paws. Apprentices leap out on one another from behind bushes and tree stumps. These are more than just games. One day, these skills could save your life and defend your Clan.

ShadowClan

SHADOWCLAN FACTS

Leader: Blackstar
Deputy: Rowanclaw
Medicine cat: Littlecloud
Hunting territory: Pine forest
Camp: Bramble-enclosed dip beneath pine trees
Unique battle skill: Night ambush

Clan character: Battle-hungry, aggressive, ambitious, and greedy for territory. It is said that the cold wind that blows across the ShadowClan territory chills their hearts and makes them suspicious and untrusting.

Prey: Frogs, lizards, and snakes that live in ShadowClan's boggy, peaty territory. A secret food source is the Twoleg garbage dump on the far boundary, although they have to be careful not to eat infected rats or crow-food.

Hunting skills: ShadowClan cats hunt by night better than other Clan cats and are skilled at skulking unseen through the undergrowth.

SIGNIFICANT LEADERS

SHADOWSTAR

Black she-cat with green eyes and thick fur.

A strategist, ferociously independent (even untrusting of Clanmates), bold in battle.

Founder of ShadowClan—worked with Thunder, Wind, and River to develop warrior code (she spent the rest of her life complaining about it).

First of founding leaders to die—losing ninth life in battle she started with other Clans.

Deputies: Unknown

Apprentices: Unknown

RAGGEDSTAR

Large dark brown tabby. Fur ragged and patchy from fighting as a kit.

Proud and cunning—failed to see his son Brokentail's blood-thirsty nature until too late.

Defeated rats in violent battle near Carrionplace that kept them from bothering ShadowClan for many moons.

Deputies: Foxheart, Cloudpelt, Brokentail (later Brokenstar)

Apprentices: Clawpaw (Clawface), Brokenpaw (Brokentail)

BROKENSTAR

Long-haired dark brown tabby with torn ears and a broad, flat face. Tail bent in middle like broken branch.

Cold, ambitious, heartless, murderous, and cruel.

Killed own father, Raggedstar.

Weakened Clan by focusing its energies on war, apprenticing kits too early, and forcing Clan to eat crow-food instead of prey.

Blinded and killed by own mother, Yellowfang.

Deputy: Blackfoot (later Blackstar)

Apprentices: Mosspaw, Volepaw (both died mysteriously before becoming warriors)

NIGHTSTAR

Elderly black tom.

Brave but frail.

Took over leadership when Brokenstar was driven into exile.

Struggled to rebuild broken Clan—StarClan did not grant him the nine lives of a leader.

Died from sickness from Carrionplace shortly after his deputy died, leaving Clan target for Tigerstar's ambitions.

Deputy: Cinderfur

Apprentice: Dawnpaw (Dawncloud)

TIGERSTAR

Large dark brown tabby tom with amber eyes and long front claws.

Ambitious, crafty, charismatic, and brilliant fighter.

Exiled by Bluestar after attempt on her life.

After period in exile, gained leadership of ShadowClan—
  rebuilding it with exceptional efficiency.

Allied ShadowClan with RiverClan to make TigerClan.

Brought BloodClan into forest at cost of many cats' lives.

Killed by Scourge, the leader of BloodClan.

Deputy: Blackfoot (later Blackstar)

Apprentice: Ravenpaw (while in ThunderClan)

BLACKSTAR

Large white tom with huge jet-black paws.

Arrogant and defensive. Tigerclaw brought him back to
  ShadowClan from exile—he still feels a hint of gratitude
  and loyalty toward the dangerous tabby.

Led Clan away from Twoleg devastation in the forest to new
  lake home.

Deputy: Russetfur

Apprentice: Tallpaw (Tallpoppy)

SIGNIFICANT MEDICINE CATS

PEBBLEHEART

Dark gray tabby tom.

Selfless, caring, desperate to help his Clanmates with any problem. Weakened himself by working tirelessly.

Realized that rats at Carrionplace were a source of infection. (Unfortunately he died from a rat-borne infection.)

RUNNINGNOSE

Small gray-and-white tom with perpetual sniffle.

Nervous and quiet. Lived long enough to retire and become an elder.

Apprentice: Littlecloud

LITTLECLOUD

Undersize brown tabby tom with light blue eyes.

Compassionate and devoted to his calling.

Close friends with ThunderClan medicine cat Cinderpelt ever since she saved his life.

As a warrior, sought help from ThunderClan during time of terrible disease. Returned with remedy that saved ShadowClan.

TAIL SIGNALS

ShadowClan was the first to devise a system of tail signals, which are now used by all Clans. Generally, the leader of a patrol is responsible for giving the signals; warriors learn to keep the leader's tail in sight at all times and react at once when an order is given.

TAIL HELD ERECT: "Stop."

TAIL RIPPLING: "Move forward with care."

TAIL HELD ERECT AND SWEEPING SLOWLY FROM SIDE TO SIDE: "Retreat silently."

TAIL POINTING LOW, PARALLEL TO GROUND, AND SWEEPING: "Spread out."

TAIL FLATTENED: "Get down."

TAIL BOBBING: "Enemy sighted."

TAIL HOOKED: "Danger."

TAIL POINTED SHARPLY: "Go that way."

TAIL HELD ERECT AND WAVING FROM SIDE TO SIDE: "Stay behind me."

TAIL KINKED OVER BACK: "Follow me."

RiverClan

RiverClan Facts

Leader: Mistystar
Deputy: Reedwhisker
Medicine cat: Mothwing
Hunting territory: The lake and streams
Camp: Overgrown island in a stream
Unique battle skill: Water combat

Clan character: Contented, sleek, well fed. Long fur and glossy coats. They love beautiful things and often collect rocks, shells, and feathers for their dens. They do not fear water.

Prey: Mainly fish but also water voles, shrews, and mice.

Hunting skills: Strong swimmers, moving silent and scentless through water. They scoop fish out of the water from the bank—a skill most cats in the other Clans cannot master.

SIGNIFICANT LEADERS

RIVERSTAR

Silvery gray, long-furred tom with green eyes.

Generous and warm-hearted with his own Clan—uninterested in the troubles of other Clans. (Would skip Gatherings if he could!)

Founder of RiverClan—worked with Thunder, Shadow, and Wind to develop warrior code.

Thought to have suggested mentoring program of training apprentices.

Deputies: Unknown

Apprentices: Unknown

CROOKEDSTAR

Huge light-colored tabby tom with green eyes and twisted jaw.

Determined, strong, and willing to bend the rules for safety of Clan.

Guided Clan through terrible leaf-bare and flood.

Accepted help from ThunderClan warriors to save Clan from starving.

Offered shelter to ThunderClan when fire drove them from their home.

Deputy: Leopardfur (later Leopardstar)

Apprentices: Graypaw (Graypool), Stonepaw (Stonefur)

LEOPARDSTAR

Spotted golden tabby she-cat.

Proud, hostile, and fierce. Single-minded about what is best for RiverClan. Showed bad judgment in turning over control of RiverClan to Tigerstar.

As deputy, she helped ThunderClan when they fled the fire in their camp.

Led her Clan to their new lake home, where she quickly established a strong base.

Deputies: Stonefur, Mistyfoot, Hawkfrost (temporarily)

Apprentices: Whitepaw (Whiteclaw), Hawkpaw (Hawkfrost)

SIGNIFICANT MEDICINE CATS

DAPPLEPELT

Delicate tortoiseshell she-cat.

Brave, reckless, quick to act.

Saw being a medicine cat as a different type of warrior, fighting the invisible enemies of sickness and injury on behalf of her Clanmates.

Saved an entire litter of kits after the nursery was washed away by a flood.

BRAMBLEBERRY

Pretty white she-cat with black-spotted fur, blue eyes, and a strikingly pink nose.

Charming, quick-thinking, and good at getting her own way—
   Crookedstar would do anything she asked.
Cautious about interpreting StarClan's omens.
Came up with a clever way to hide medicinal herbs in fresh-kill
   so sick kits would eat them.

MUDFUR

Long-haired, light brown tom.
Patient, intelligent, and straightforward.
Interpreted moth's wing sign to choose his new apprentice,
   despite her non-Clan origins.

MOTHWING

Beautiful dappled-golden she-cat with large amber eyes in a
   triangular face, and a long pelt rippling with dark tabby
   stripes.
The daughter of a rogue cat, Sasha, and the former leader of
   ShadowClan, Tigerstar, Mothwing struggles for acceptance by
   her Clan.
Believes StarClan does not exist.
With Leafpool's help, healed her Clan when kits brought traces of
   Twoleg poison back to camp.

WATER COMBAT MOVES

RiverClan warriors have developed special techniques for fighting in the water. The water techniques are a closely guarded secret among RiverClan cats, so all training is done out of sight, along the streams that run through the territory.

DOUBLE-FRONT-PAW SLAP-DOWN: Splashes water into the face of the enemy.

UNDERWATER LEG SWEEP (FRONT OR HIND): The opponent will not see it coming under the water so won't have a chance to brace himself before losing his balance.

PUSH-DOWN AND RELEASE: Almost all non-RiverClan cats panic if they are submerged, while RiverClan cats know how to hold their breath underwater. This move can be used to secure a decisive victory, because it's most likely to make the opponent surrender.

UNDERWATER CLINCH: Uses warrior's weight to hold the opponent below the surface, with a firm grip that enables the warrior to bring his enemy spluttering back to the surface before forcing him under again.

TAIL SPLASH: Temporarily blinds opponent by flicking water in his eyes.

UNDERWATER PUSH-OFF: Crouching and erupting out of the water into opponent, using surprise and impact to knock him off balance.

RUSHPAW SPLASH: Using noise of water splashed at a distance to create a decoy, leaving opportunity for a surprise attack.

WindClan

Leader: Onestar
Deputy: Ashfoot
Medicine cat: Kestrelflight
Hunting territory: The open hillside
Camp: Shallow scoop in hillside
Unique battle skill: Speed and agility

Clan character: Fiercely loyal, tough, fast-running, and easily offended cats. They are nervous and quick to flee, due to the lack of cover on the open moor. Of all the Clans, they have the deepest knowledge of Twolegs from seeing them on the nearby farms.

Prey: Mainly rabbits.

Hunting skills: Fast, lean, and swift. Their short, smooth pelts of browns and grays blend in with the rocks and grasses.

SIGNIFICANT LEADERS

WINDSTAR

Wiry brown she-cat with yellow eyes.

Proud, wily, stubborn, and fastest cat in the forest.

Founder of WindClan—worked with Thunder, Shadow, and
River to develop warrior code.

Many of her descendants run with Clan today, including current
deputy, Ashfoot, and Ashfoot's son Crowfeather.

Deputies: Gorsefur (later Gorsestar)

Apprentices: Unknown

GORSESTAR

Thin gray tabby cat.

Remembered for his bravery and devotion to Windstar, his mate.

Deputies: Unknown

Apprentices: Unknown

TALLSTAR

Black-and-white tom with long tail and amber eyes.

One of the wisest and longest-lived WindClan leaders.

Unusually close to ThunderClan and particularly their leader
   Firestar.
Watched over Clan as they were forced out of home by
   ShadowClan.
One of first cats to argue for leaving the forest, according to the
   prophecy. Frail and on last life, he led Clan to new home.
On his deathbed, Tallstar changed his deputy from Mudclaw to
   Onewhisker—a wise choice in the long run.
Deputies: Deadfoot, Mudclaw, Onewhisker (later Onestar)
Apprentice: Morningpaw (Morningflower)

ONESTAR

Small, mottled-brown tabby tom.
Loyal, devoted, strong, and compassionate.
Guided Clan through time of terrible tension after Tallstar made
   him leader in Mudclaw's place.
Survived rebellion against him.
First leader to receive nine lives at the Moonpool.
Took warriors to save ThunderClan when the badgers attacked.
Deputy: Ashfoot
Apprentices: Whitepaw (Whitetail), Gorsepaw (Gorsetail)

SIGNIFICANT MEDICINE CATS

MOTHFLIGHT

Soft white fur and stormy green eyes.

First WindClan medicine cat.

Loyal and true to her Clan, her restlessness, curiosity, and
dreaminess were at first deemed unwarriorlike.

These qualities gave her a new destiny, leading her to the
Moonstone.

THRUSHPELT

Stone-gray she-cat with flecks of darker brown fur.

Warrior for several moons before becoming WindClan
medicine cat.

Interpreted signs with immense confidence.

Expert herb finder.

Temperamental and quick to fight.

Took care of Clan through a sick-rabbit epidemic.

BARKFACE

Brown tom with stumpy tail.

Reliable, practical, and efficient.

Long, dependable service.

Received prophecy foretelling death at Gorge after WindClan
returned home.

SPECIAL BATTLE TACTICS

Graywing the Wise led WindClan many, many moons ago, before "star" was added to leaders' names. He won the reputation for being the greatest leader of any Clan, thanks to his attention to battle strategy. He realized that the most important element of any battle was the position of warriors before and during combat. Using small stones and marks made by sticks on the floor of his den, he developed tactics for every sort of battle, even on WindClan's open moorland territory, where there were no natural hiding places or traps.

1. APPROACH FROM ABOVE YOUR ENEMY.

The advantage of gaining the higher ground is that you can charge at greater speed at the enemy, who will be weakened by having to fight uphill.

2. USE THE LIGHT FROM THE SUN.

The sun should be behind you to dazzle the enemy. In greenleaf, the midday sun is especially bright and cruel to cats who are used to skulking under the cover of trees. In leaf-bare, the low sun hovers around the eye line like a troublesome bee; keep your enemies facing it, and they'll have trouble seeing an attack from any direction.

3. KNOW WHERE THE WIND IS COMING FROM.

If there is a strong wind, it should blow from behind you toward the enemy, blinding them with dust and holding them back like the current of a river. If you wish to preserve the element of surprise, the wind should blow from the enemy position toward you so that your scent is carried away from them.

4. CONCEAL THE SIZE OF YOUR FORCE.

The number of cats in your battle patrols can be hidden to confuse the enemy from a distance. Cats packed tightly together will appear as a small attacking force, encouraging the enemy to be overconfident and make poor strategic decisions. Alternatively, if cats are spread out single file, they will look like a solid border of warriors, which will seem impenetrable to an advancing enemy.

5. ATTACK BOTH ENDS OF THE ENEMY LINE FIRST.

If both ends of the enemy's line are defeated, the cats in the center of the line will have to fight on two fronts. Even if they are not outnumbered, they will be outflanked, vulnerable, and in disarray.

6. KEEP FRESH WARRIORS IN RESERVE.

Always have adequate reserves of fresh, fit warriors behind the battle line. They will be able to replace injured warriors, launch a separate attack if the enemy tries to encircle your forces, or fend off a surprise enemy from the rear. If the battle is in your favor, finish it by sending your reserve warriors behind the enemy line to surround them and demand surrender.

7. FEIGNED RETREAT AND AMBUSH.

A group of strong cats charges at the enemy, screeching, then turns around and withdraws. Repeat this until the infuriated enemy finally breaks its line and gives chase. Then the trap is sprung. Other warriors positioned in rabbit holes and in dips in the ground—out of the enemies' eye line—attack as soon as your opponents have gone past. The enemy will be forced to stop and turn around to fight this unexpected threat, and as they do the retreating cats must turn and charge back at them at full speed. The enemy is caught between two bodies of attacking cats and will quickly surrender.

SKYCLAN

SKYCLAN FACTS

Leader: Leafstar
Deputy: Sharpclaw
Medicine cat: Echosong
Hunting territory: A sandy gorge
Camp: Caves in wall of gorge
Unique battle skill: Aboveground combat

Clan character: Quiet, private, and thoughtful. The position of their territory so close to Twolegplace makes them more focused on external threats (such as kittypets, dogs, and Twolegs). They are the most likely to seek a peaceful solution to interClan disputes.

Prey: Birds and squirrels, anything that nests or feeds in trees. Song thrushes are a particular favorite.

Hunting skills: Unique ability to jump high into the air. This enables them to leap into trees that lack lower branches and get into spots where birds and squirrels might otherwise feel safe. They prefer hunting aboveground to such an extent that their stalking skills are minimal.

ABOVEGROUND BATTLE MOVES

It is a matter of great pride to SkyClan apprentices that they can carry out the Sky-drop, as well as these other moves.

THE SKY-CRUSHER: Landing with all four feet on top of an opponent, flattening him like a leaf.

THE FLICK-OVER: Landing with front paws outstretched to sweep the opponent off his feet and roll him onto his back.

THE KICK: Kicking down hard as the warrior nears the ground, then using momentum from landing to spring away before the opponent can retaliate.

THE SLICE: Dropping down with claws unsheathed for maximum injury.

THE BRANCH SWING: Holding on to branch with front claws and swinging hind legs into the opponent's face.

THE REVERSE BRANCH SWING: Holding on to branch with hind claws and striking with front legs through the swing.

THE TRUNK SPRING: Sliding down trunk and springing off at head height, using hind legs to push off and clear opponents (good if tree is surrounded).

THE REVERSE CLIMB: Climbing backward up the trunk as the opponent advances to gain advantage of height; often followed by Trunk Spring.

IMPORTANT MEDICINES
AND THEIR USES

BORAGE LEAVES To be chewed and eaten. The plant can be distinguished by its small blue or pink star-shaped flowers and hairy leaves. Great for nursing queens as it helps increase their supply of milk. Also brings down fever.

BURDOCK ROOT A tall-stemmed, sharp-smelling thistle with dark leaves. A medicine cat must dig up the roots, wash off the dirt, and chew them into a pulp, which can be applied to rat bites. Cures infection.

CATMINT (also known as catnip) A delicious-smelling, leafy plant that's hard to find in the wild; often found growing in Twoleg gardens. The best remedy for greencough.

CHERVIL A sweet-smelling plant with large, spreading, fernlike leaves and small white flowers. The juice of the leaves can be used for infected wounds, and chewing the roots helps with bellyache.

COBWEB Spiderwebs can be found all over the forest; be careful not to bring along the spider when you take the web! Medicine cats wrap it around an injury to soak up the blood and keep the wound clean. Stops bleeding.

COLTSFOOT A flowering plant, a bit like a dandelion, with yellow or white flowers. The leaves can be chewed into a pulp, which is eaten to help shortness of breath.

COMFREY Identifiable by its large leaves and small bell-shaped flowers, which can be pink, white, or purple. The fat black roots of this plant can be chewed into a poultice to mend broken bones or soothe wounds.

DOCK A plant similar to sorrel. The leaf can be chewed up and applied to soothe scratches.

DRIED OAK LEAF Collected in the autumn and stored in a dry place. Stops infections.

FEVERFEW A small bush with flowers like daisies. The leaves can be eaten to cool down body temperature, particularly for cats with fever or chills.

GOLDENROD A tall plant with bright yellow flowers. A poultice of this is terrific for healing wounds.

HONEY A sweet, golden liquid created by bees. Difficult to collect without getting stung, but great for soothing infections or the throats of cats who have breathed smoke.

HORSETAIL A tall plant with bristly stems that grows in marshy areas. The leaves can be used to treat infected wounds. Usually chewed up and applied as a poultice.

JUNIPER BERRIES A bush with spiky dark green leaves and purple berries. The berries soothe bellyaches and help cats who are having trouble breathing.

LAVENDER A small purple flowering plant. Cures fever.

MARIGOLD A bright orange or yellow flower that grows low to the ground. The petals or leaves can be chewed into a pulp and applied as a poultice to wounds. Stops infection.

MOUSE BILE A bad-smelling liquid that is the only remedy for ticks. Dab a little moss soaked in bile on a tick and it'll fall right off. Wash paws thoroughly in running water afterward.

POPPY SEED Small black seeds shaken from a dried poppy flower, these are fed to cats to help them sleep. Soothes cats suffering from shock and distress. Not recommended for nursing queens.

STINGING NETTLE The spiny green seeds can be administered to a cat who's swallowed poison, while the leaves can be applied to a wound to bring down swelling.

TANSY A strong-smelling plant with round yellow flowers. Good for curing coughs, but must be eaten in small doses.

THYME This herb can be eaten to calm anxiety and frayed nerves.

WATERMINT A leafy green plant found in streams or damp earth. Usually chewed into a pulp and then fed to a cat suffering bellyache.

WILD GARLIC Rolling in a patch of wild garlic can help prevent infection, especially for dangerous wounds like rat bites.

YARROW A flowering plant whose leaves can be made into a poultice and applied to wounds or scratches to expel poison.

NOTE:

DEATHBERRIES Red berries that can be fatally poisonous to kits and elders. They are NOT a medicine. Known to Twolegs as yew berries. BEWARE!

OTHER ANIMALS

FOXES

Russet-red fur, bushy tails, sharp teeth, and pointed noses. Look
a bit like dogs.

Live in dens, often in sandy ground hidden by undergrowth.

Live alone or with their cubs.

Mean, suspicious, and hostile, they don't eat cats, but they will
kill for pleasure and not just for prey.

They hunt mostly at night and have a strong and unpleasant
smell.

BADGERS

Large, with short black fur and a white stripe down their long,
pointed muzzles.

Small, beady eyes, powerful shoulders, and sharp claws.

Live in either caves or sets, which are tunnels underground,
bushes, or tree roots.

Live alone or with their kits and have a very distinctive smell.

Badgers sometimes prey on young cat kits. Can trample their
victims with enormous paws or deliver a deadly bite.

Have tremendously powerful jaws that make it nearly impossible to escape their grip.

Midnight: An exceptional badger at the sun-drown-place. She has no hostility for cats. She has a special connection with StarClan and can speak both Cat and Fox. It was Midnight who passed on the message that the Clans must leave the forest.

DOGS

Size varies from that of a kit to a pony. Fur can be long or short, white, brown, black, gray, or a mix. Can have pointy or flat noses, droopy or sharp ears. Make loud, angry noises and love chasing cats.

Live mostly in Twoleg nests or barns. Wild dogs might sleep anywhere; one pack in recent Clan history made their home in the caves below Snakerocks.

Loud, fast, and sharp-toothed. Many dogs seem to be devoted to their Twolegs and are seen only in Twoleg company. There is a theory that most dogs are too dim-witted to be truly dangerous. Packs of dogs are always to be feared.

BIRDS OF PREY

Winged predators with hooked beaks and sharp, curving talons,
   these include hawks, eagles, falcons, and owls.
Nest in hollows or branches of trees, or on the ledges of cliffs.
Extremely sharp vision for spotting prey from a distance. Hawks
   and eagles are daytime hunters; owls hunt at night. They
   swoop down from the sky to carry off prey, which includes
   kits. This was the fate of Snowkit, Speckletail's deaf son,
   when a hawk attacked the camp after a forest fire had
   burned away its protective cover. The Tribe of Rushing
   Water have developed clever ways to hunt these birds.

HORSES/SHEEP/COWS

Four-legged farm creatures.
Horses are tall and swift with flowing manes and tails and
   giant, pounding hooves.
Sheep look like fluffy white clouds dotted across a green field.
Cows can be black and white or brown,
   and their hooves are to be avoided.
Live in large fenced fields and sometimes hay-filled
      Twoleg barns.
Mostly harmless. However, take caution passing through their
   fields. A galloping horse or stampeding herd of cows would
   trample a cat without even noticing.

RATS

Brown-furred and beady-eyed rodents, with long, naked tails
and sharp front teeth. Not much bigger than kits.

Live in garbage dumps like Carrionplace in ShadowClan
territory or anywhere they can scavenge Twoleg food.

Live and travel in packs. Individually they pose no threat to
cats, but their numbers are often overwhelming, and bites
can cause infection. A single rat contaminated the whole of
ShadowClan during Nightstar's brief time as leader.

TWOLEGS

Tall, smooth-skinned creatures with some fur on their heads.
Walk on two legs.

Live in large, boxy nests with hard roofs and floors, often
surrounded by tidy gardens and fences.

Also known as Nofurs or Upwalkers. Twolegs ride around in
monsters and seem to like dogs. They are to be avoided if
possible, as they are capable of doing something
unpredictable at any moment, such as tearing down a tree,
starting a fire, or locking up a cat for no reason.

The Forest Territories

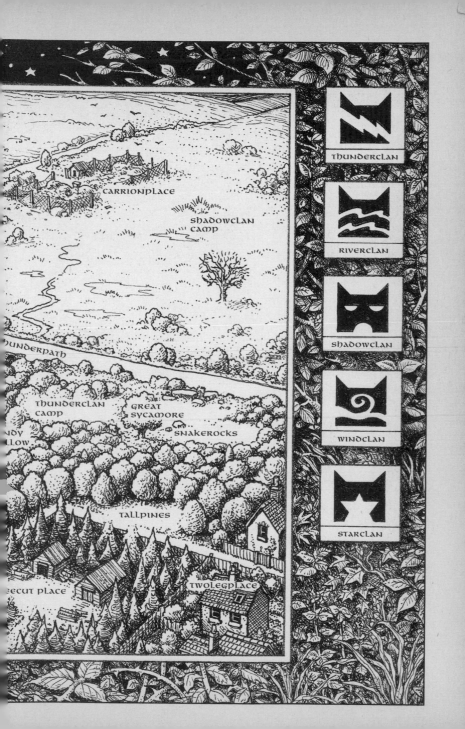

CARRIONPLACE

SHADOWCLAN
CAMP

THUNDERPATH

THUNDERCLAN
CAMP

GREAT
SYCAMORE

SNAKEROCKS

NDY
LLOW

TALLPINES

EECUT PLACE

TWOLEGPLACE

THUNDERCLAN

RIVERCLAN

SHADOWCLAN

WINDCLAN

STARCLAN

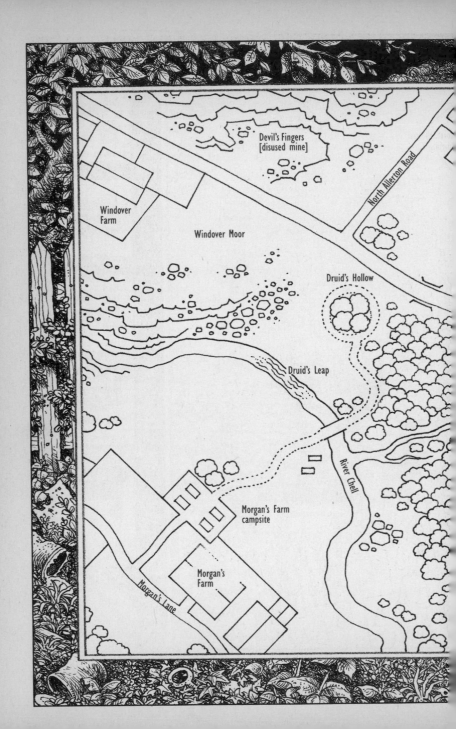

Devil's Fingers
[disused mine]

North Allerton Road

Windover
Farm

Windover Moor

Druid's Hollow

Druid's Leap

River Chell

Morgan's Farm
campsite

Morgan's
Farm

Morgan's Lane

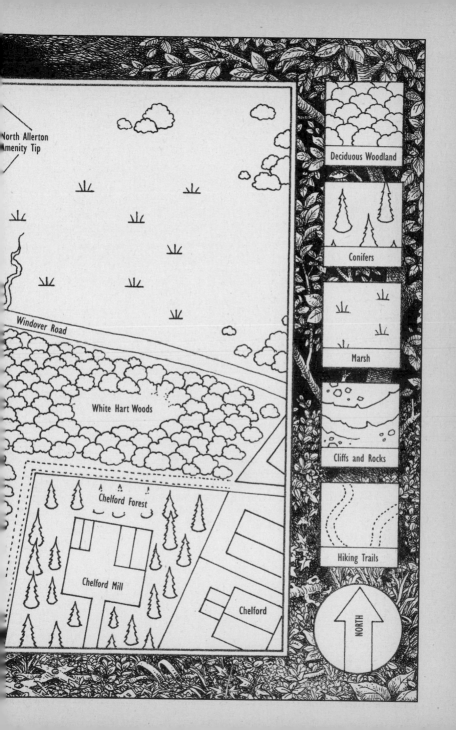

North Allerton Amenity Tip

Windover Road

White Hart Woods

Chelford Forest

Chelford Mill

Chelford

Deciduous Woodland

Conifers

Marsh

Cliffs and Rocks

Hiking Trails

NORTH

THUNDERCLAN FOREST CAMP

Welcome to ThunderClan's forest camp! I'm Sandstorm, a ThunderClan warrior. Firestar has asked me to show you around. Watch out, though. Some of the elders might be cranky if we disturb them while they're having a nap.

Can you see the camp entrance? Well hidden, isn't it? Those brambles protect us from predators, but they don't stop the sunshine from warming up the camp.

Follow me down the ravine. Bluestar says it used to be a river a long time ago, but I can't imagine that. It's so dry and sandy now. Keep your head down—we're going through this tunnel in the gorse. See the path under your paws? Hundreds of ThunderClan cats have been this way over many generations. Watch out for the prickles!

And here we are! No, Squirrelpaw, this is my guest. They didn't sneak up behind me. Yes, I know you're standing guard. I'm sure the whole camp knows we're here now.

Over this way is the nursery. See the thick bramble walls? The nursery is the strongest part of the Clan camp. Can you hear the kits mewing and playing inside? Queens and warriors will fight like TigerClan to protect them.

Notice the clump of ferns beside the tree stump? That's where the apprentices sleep. It's supposed to be lined with moss, but it looks like a certain apprentice has kicked up a bit of a mess. After guard duty, I promise you she will be cleaning it up. Poor Squirrelpaw! She has always been such a restless sleeper.

Warriors sleep under that bush—you can see the entrance tunnel there. As a senior warrior, I sleep in the center of the group, where it's warmest. I remember being a young warrior, though. It can get cold on the edge during leaf-bare!

This fallen tree is the elders' den. Go ahead, poke your nose inside. Oh, sorry, Dappletail! I'm giving a tour. No, they are not spying for ShadowClan! Don't you have an apprentice to torment, Dappletail?

Quickly, while she's gone, put your paws on the den floor. Don't the grass and moss feel soft? The apprentices keep it fresh. Nobody wants grumpy elders . . . well, no grumpier than usual.

Let's cross the clearing to that tall, smooth boulder over there. This is Highrock, and it's where our leader stands to make announcements to the whole Clan and to lead ceremonies. Can you picture it? You'd listen, wouldn't you?

Around here is Firestar's den. Hello? Firestar? He must be out on patrol. Peek through the lichen hanging over the entrance. This is where he sleeps. Before him it was Bluestar, and after him, who knows? Firepaw was a pudgy little kittypet when I first met him. Who could ever have dreamed he'd be our leader?

Before you go, let me show you the medicine cat's den. Come inside. I love the smell of the herbs. Leafpaw! That's my other daughter—she's in training to be a medicine cat, and she's very clever. She sleeps at this end of the fern tunnel. Her mentor, Cinderpelt, sleeps in that hole in the rock over there. Leafpaw! There you are. Always sorting herbs! She's so dedicated and hard-working. It makes me very proud.

What's that? You think your sister would rather be hunting than on guard duty? All right, I'll have a word with Firestar and see if she can come to the Gathering tonight—that should cheer her up.

And that's our camp! I should really be off hunting now. Watch your fur on the way out. And don't tell anyone you were here!

THUNDERCLAN FOREST TERRITORY

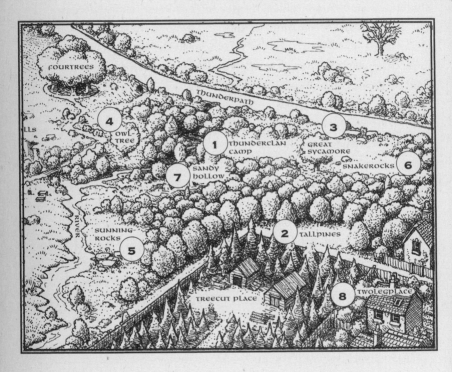

(1) **ThunderClan camp:** Sheltered at the foot of a sandy ravine and well protected by thornbushes, this camp is hard to attack and easy to defend.

(2) **Tallpines:** Watch out for the Twoleg tree-eater! It makes the ground rumble and leaves deep gullies that fill with muddy water.

(3) **Great Sycamore:** Its branches are thick and strong all the way to the ends. Young apprentices learn to climb here and dare one another to climb higher.

(4) **Owl-Tree:** Halfway up the trunk is a hole that is home to a tawny owl that flies out at night. Legend has it that an early ThunderClan apprentice learned the secrets of night hunting from one such owl. Every night, as the moon rose, he would wait at the foot of the Owl-Tree. When the owl swooped out, he followed, like the owl's shadow cast by the moon on the ground. Eventually this bold young apprentice became a great leader known as Owlstar. In the hunt, he was as silent and deadly as the tawny owl.

(5) **Sunningrocks:** A warm spot in the sunshine. Keep a sharp eye out for prey darting between the cracks! Many moons ago, when the river was much wider than it is now, Sunningrocks was an island. Only RiverClan cats could swim out to it. Then the water dropped, and Sunningrocks became part of the forest shore, so ThunderClan claimed it. They did not allow RiverClan cats to cross their territory to reach it. Since then, many battles have been fought between the two Clans over these smooth, sun-warmed stones.

(6) **Snakerocks:** Beware poisonous adders! Chervil grows abundantly here. The caves beneath the rocks provide shelter for dangerous animals, like foxes, badgers—and even dogs.

(7) **Sandy hollow:** A training hollow surrounded by trees. Warrior apprentices are unlikely to hurt themselves on the soft ground.

(8) **Twolegplace:** A maze of small Thunderpaths and Twoleg dens (see *Other Animals, Twolegs*). There are two different kinds of cats in Twolegplace: loners and kittypets (see *Cats Outside the Clans, Rogues and Loners,* and *Kittypets*).

shadowclan forest camp

My name is Boulder. Ah, I can see you've realized it's not a warrior name. Well, I used to be a loner in Twolegplace, and proud of it. I caught prey for myself. I could look after myself. Then I met a cat from ShadowClan. He told me about the forest. He wanted me to give up my freedom and join his Clanmates! I nearly clawed off his fur. I didn't need a leader or a Clan.

But he kept talking, and some of the things he said made sense. Like, what was I going to do when I was old and couldn't catch my own prey? I'd never thought about that before.

I agreed to visit his camp. Follow me, and you'll see what I saw on that day I first came to the forest. I've never left since.

I love the forest on this side of the Thunderpath. The soft carpet of pine needles under my paws. The fresh and sharp smell of the pines. The boggy soil is full of amazing smells; can you sense prey darting around under the leaves?

Through these brambles, that's right. This tiny path—here, where my paws are—leads to a hollow. I know it's not exactly grassy around here, but the ground is muddy and cool. Good for keeping fresh-kill fresh. Our leader sleeps over there, beneath the roots of that big oak tree. The warriors' den is over there, underneath the bramble bush. I know it looks prickly on the outside, but inside it's lined with pine needles and moss. I can tell you, it's a lot more comfortable than any place I found to stretch my paws in Twolegplace.

The smooth boulder at the edge of the clearing is where the leader speaks to us. Do you see that other rock propped against it, creating a sheltered half cave underneath? That's where the medicine cat lives. There are holes dug in the ground to keep the leaves and berries fresh, and sick cats can rest in the ferns that grow on the other side of the boulders. I never had another cat care about my injuries when I lived in Twolegplace.

The nursery's over there, in that hollow shielded by a thornbush. You can smell the scent of milk from here—a new litter was born yesterday. I don't spend much time with the tiniest kits—always worried I'll step on them or something—but I like watching them grow into strong apprentices and loyal warriors.

Why do you keep staring at the fresh-kill pile? Oh, I see you've spotted a frog. I know they look pretty unappetizing—trust me, I was as reluctant as you to try them when I first came to the forest. But you should try them. Peel off the skin first—that's very chewy. Underneath, it tastes like if you mixed rabbits and fish together. Honestly! Well, okay, maybe leave it for one of the warriors. Look, I know the other Clans think ShadowClan cats are strange and dark-hearted, but we're loyal warriors, just like them. There's no need to fear us.

Not all of the time, anyway.

ShadowClan Forest Territory

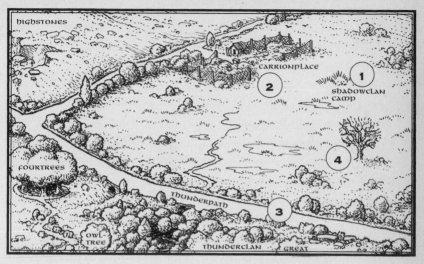

(1) ShadowClan camp: A dark, well-concealed hollow, the camp is hidden deep in the shadows and is surrounded by brambles as prickly and fierce as the hearts of ShadowClan warriors.

(2) Carrionplace: Yuck! Smell that? This is an evil place where rats and disease lurk.

(3) Thunderpath tunnel: The ability of ShadowClan cats to move freely across the most feared border of the Thunderpath has enhanced their reputation for mysterious strength and invincibility.

(4) Burnt Sycamore: An ancient tree destroyed by lightning many moons ago. Apprentices are often trained here to hunt at night and stalk noiselessly through the undergrowth.

RIVERCLAN FOREST CAMP

hi, I'm Feathertail. You'll have to get your paws wet if you want to see our camp. It's on an island! Don't be afraid of crossing; just listen to the murmur of the river—it's very soothing.

Under these long, trailing branches, that's right. They are willow trees. You should see them in leaf-bare after a frost. They sparkle like frozen raindrops!

All right, shake your paws, duck your head, and follow me through the reeds. The whole camp is surrounded by reeds, murmuring in the breeze. I love the sound they make, under the burble of the water. Look! It's our camp!

Here, in this central clearing, we lie in the sun and share tongues. In the mornings, I lie here and dry my fur after an early patrol. It's my favorite spot in the whole camp.

Here's the warriors' den, in this tangle of reeds. It's next to the nursery to protect the kits. Poke your head inside—it's all right; all the warriors are on patrol.

Look up at the roof of the den. See how we've woven feathers into the branches? And along the edges are sparkling rocks and shells from the river. They make the den shimmer, don't they? I love to lie in here, watching the lights and colors. It's just as beautiful in the nursery.

See how close the river comes to the nursery? Here, it's shallow and safe, but once before I was born, the river rose up suddenly and swept away the floor of the nursery and two kits—my mentor's kits. Now the walls are stronger. We like to have the kits living near water. They inherit our love of it and learn to swim quickly. Oh, look, they are practicing now!

You are doing wonderfully, kittens! Soon you'll be swimming faster than I can!

Across the clearing are the other dens, including Mudfur's— he's our medicine cat. Peek inside. You'll see that he makes small caves in the earth for the herbs. Now the kits can't scatter them when they run through his den chasing frogs.

On the other side of the island, a couple of rocks stick out of the river when the water isn't too high. They soak up the warmth of the sun. My favorite days begin with hunting with my brother, Stormfur, and end in the sun on those rocks. But you have to be fast. There is space for only a couple of cats, and if senior warriors or elders want them, you're out of luck. Our whole Clan could fit on Sunningrocks, where we used to bask. There was even room left for chasing prey and play-fighting. But I won't get into that now!

Uh-oh, it looks like rain. I'm going to curl up in the warriors' den and listen to the raindrops on the roof.

You should probably go too. But thank you for visiting!

RIVERCLAN FOREST TERRITORY

(1) RiverClan camp: This well-drained island is circled by gently rustling reeds instead of thorns, but the other Clans' hatred of water means that it has never been attacked.

(2) The gorge: See *WindClan Forest Territory*.

(3) The river: It is a source of prey and protection to RiverClan, yet it is as changeable as the moon. Sometimes it is quiet, gentle, and murmuring, but sometimes it froths and roars like a Twoleg monster.

(4) Twoleg bridge: A safe way to cross the river and get to Fourtrees when the water is high.

WINDCLAN FOREST CAMP

Welcome to our camp! I'm Onewhisker, a warrior in WindClan, the greatest Clan in the forest.

You couldn't see our camp as you came this way, could you? That's because it's hidden in the only sheltered spot on the moor. It's a sandy hollow in the ground, surrounded by a tangle of gorse. The elders say that our first leader, Windstar, reached down from StarClan and scooped out a pawful of sand to make a hollow for us to live in.

Press through the prickly branches here and you'll be able to see the center of the camp. Breathe deeply. Don't you love the fresh air? It's so full of life and energy. I don't know how those other Clan cats live where they do. If I couldn't see the sky all day and all night, I'd go mad!

That's why the warriors sleep out here, under the stars, where our warrior ancestors can see us. It gives us a special connection to StarClan. We've had to deal with a lot of trouble and danger, but when I see them up there before I close my eyes, I know they're watching out for us.

Elders and kits can't sleep out in the open, though, so we've built dens for them along the edge of the gorse wall. And the leader has a den back behind the Tallrock, too, but he doesn't usually sleep there. Tallstar likes to sleep out in the open with us. What's the Tallrock? Oh, it's that large boulder over there from where Tallstar makes announcements and conducts ceremonies.

Hear that? It's an apprentice calling from Outlook Rock. That means there are trespassers in our territory! I'd better go chase them out.

Thanks for visiting!

WINDCLAN FOREST TERRITORY

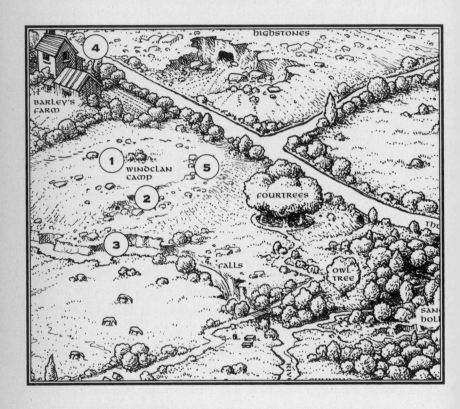

(1) WindClan camp: Tucked into a natural dip in the sandy moor, this camp is sheltered from the wind but has proved vulnerable to attack.

(2) Abandoned badger set: WindClan apprentices used to come here to learn the scent of badger. Now a great spot for hunting rabbits!

(3) **The gorge:** WindClan elders boast that they leaped all the way across in their youth, but apprentices are strictly forbidden to go too close.

(4) **Twoleg farm:** Cows, sheep, dogs, Twolegs, and two loner cats named Barley and Ravenpaw live here. WindClan sheltered in the barn on their way home from exile.

(5) **Outlook Rock:** This large, flat, gray stone slopes steeply above the level moors. From here, you can spot movement far across the grassland, especially a slow-moving or brightly colored cat from another Clan. WindClan apprentices are assigned to Outlook Rock to test their alertness and guard-duty skills.

The Lake Territories

GREENLEAF
TWOLEGPLACE

CLEARING

TWOLEG
NEST

TWOLEG PATH

TWOLEG PATH

SHADOWCLAN
CAMP

HALFBRIDGE

SMALL
THUNDERPATH

GREENLEAF
TWOLEGPLACE

HALFBRIDGE

ISLAND

STREAM

RIVERCLAN
CAMP

Hareview Campsite

Sanctuary
Cottage

Sadler Woods

Littlepine Road

Littlepine
Sailing
Center

Littlepine
Island

River Alba

Whitchurch Road

Abandoned Workman's House

Quarry Road [disused]

Crystal Pool

Quarry

Hare Hill Woods

Hare Hill

Sanctuary Lake

Hare Hill Riding Stables

Hare Hill Road

Knight's Copse

Deciduous Woodland

Pine Forest

Marsh

Lake

Footpaths

NORTH

THUNDERCLAN LAKE CAMP

hi! I'm Squirrelflight. I'm going to show you our new camp by the lake! It's perfect, and you know what? I found it!

I'll show you how I did it. Let's creep through these thornbushes here . . . okay, stop! Careful! You nearly did what I did, didn't you? Only I was running really fast after a vole. And suddenly—WHOMP! I took off through the air! And then I landed in a pile of brambles! Here, lie on your belly and peek over the edge of the cliff. See that bush down there? That's where I landed. Ouch!

But actually, I was lucky. If I'd tripped over that side instead, I would have had much farther to fall. These walls around the camp are tall and stone and hard to climb. Here, slide along this wall. Completely smooth, right? Isn't that weird? We think Twolegs were here a long time ago, slicing stone off the walls with their monsters. Don't ask me why! Twolegs are so mouse-brained.

Luckily they've gone away, and now there are lots of bushes and trees growing up over this hollow to protect us. The stone walls keep out the wind, although we have to watch our step near the edge. Brambleclaw keeps lecturing me about that. You'd think I was a newborn kit the way he talks to me!

All right, duck your head and squeeze through this thorn barrier. Intimidating, isn't it? If you were a ShadowClan cat, you'd probably turn tail rather than attack, wouldn't you?

Behold our beautiful camp! Isn't it amazing? Isn't it perfect? Did I mention that I found it? You've come at a good time—it's sunhigh, so lots of cats are sleeping. Look at grumpy old Mousefur over there, snoring away. The cat next to her with his nose in the air is Longtail. He's blind, but he can probably smell you; that's why he looks anxious. Don't be offended. Not every cat smells as great as ThunderClan.

Jump up on these rocks here—watch your claws; the rocks can be slippery. Now we're standing on the Highledge. You can see the whole camp! Firestar makes his announcements from up here. He puffs out his chest like this, and he struts forward like this, and then he opens his mouth and yowls: "Let all those cats old enough to catch their own prey join—"

Uh-oh. I think I did that a bit louder than I meant to. Here come Cloudtail, Dustpelt, and Brambleclaw. Quick, into Firestar's den! Oh, come on, move your fur, it's just a cave. In, in, in!

Isn't it cool in here? It's so dim and shady. Firestar sleeps back here on this bed of ferns and moss. It looks soft and springy. I

don't know how he keeps it so neat all the time. Doesn't it make you want to jump on it and roll around? Oops! I thought it would hold up better than that. Do you think he'll notice? Maybe we should get out of here.

See the caves where the apprentices and the elders sleep? The warriors—like me!—sleep under that big thornbush over there. Under the biggest bramble thicket is the nursery. Want to visit my friend Sorreltail? She has the cutest kits in the world. Come on, let's go over and stick our noses in.

Hello, Sorreltail. Hi, kittens! Oh, Sorreltail does look sleepy. Sorry, we'll let you get back to napping.

Across the camp is the medicine cat's den. Hurry, Brambleclaw is coming with his extra-grumpy face on. What cute kits! I don't want any of my own yet, though. I want to do a lot more warrior stuff first. Although it does look comfortable in the nursery.

You can't see the den here because it's hidden by this curtain of hanging bramble tendrils. But slip through it and—see? Look at this great cave! Hey, Leafpool, how's it going? My sister is our medicine cat. The smell in here always makes me sneeze. Achoo! Oops, sorry, Leafpool . . . were those supposed to be stacked like that? Look, this is my friend. I wanted to show how nice it is in here. It almost makes you want to get sick. The sand is really soft, and there's a little pool in the back for water. Leafpool stores her herbs in these cracks in the wall, or, I guess, out here in a pile where any cat can step on them. What? I didn't do it on purpose!

Uh-oh—hear that yowling? That's our bossy tabby friend looking for me. Perhaps you'd better go. Tell you what, I'll jump on him, and you make a dash for the tunnel. Then you might want to keep running as far and as fast as you can. Brambleclaw can be very serious about scaring off trespassers. Okay, ready? All right, go! Run! Quick as you can!

ThunderClan Lake
Territory

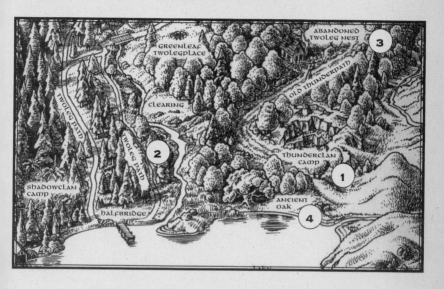

(1) **ThunderClan camp:** This symmetrical stone hollow, enclosed by towering cliffs of sheer stone left behind by Twolegs, was the obvious choice for ThunderClan's new camp.

(2) **Twoleg paths:** Twolegs mark their paths with shiny blue markers!

(3) **Abandoned Twoleg nest:** A good place for prey and an excellent source of herbs. It has an ominous, empty feeling and seems ready to fall down at any moment.

(4) **Ancient Oak:** In an old rabbit burrow below the twisting roots, Brambleclaw, Mistyfoot, Crowfeather, Tawnypelt, and Squirrelpaw sheltered on their first trip around the lake, scouting for new Clan territories and camps. Also known as Sky Oak.

shadowclan lake camp

I never thought Blackstar would let you into the ShadowClan camp. He's a little prickly mostly. But we like having a cat in charge who says exactly what he thinks.

I'm Tawnypelt, and I found this place—you've heard about that?

I tell you, by the time we found the camp, I was getting worried. The territory looked right—pine trees everywhere, shadows, and darkness. But the tree branches were much higher than we were used to, and there wasn't much undergrowth.

It was getting dark when we came up this slope here. Did you see the pool down at the bottom? It's close to the camp so we can fetch water for the elders and kits without having to go all the way to the lake. Here, follow me up these boulders until we get to that top one—it's got the best view of the camp.

Great, isn't it? You can barely tell there are so many cats down there, hidden below the tangles of brambles. And look at all these low-hanging branches all around and above us. You won't catch us getting trampled by badgers like ThunderClan!

Not that we're cowards, mind you. Every ShadowClan cat, down to the tiniest kit, will fight to the death to defend our territory and our pride. We're the fiercest Clan in the forest, no matter what any other cat might say.

I wasn't born a ShadowClan cat—but I'm very glad I'm here now. I like being ferocious, and I like hunting in the dark. You won't find me lolling around in the sun like those RiverClan cats or crashing through the forest making as much noise as a ThunderClan cat.

But we can have fun too. Smokepaw and I like to climb trees near the lake and watch the Twolegs on the water. Their boats look like swan wings. The Twolegs make a lot of noise and splashing, and sometimes the boats tip over and they fall in! Then they get back up and fluff out their wings to try again. You've never seen anything so funny. I would never set paw on a boat—leave that to the RiverClan cats!

Anyway, slip on through these bramble bushes and you can

see the camp. Like in the old camp, there is a clear progression of dens from one side to the other: nursery first, then the apprentices' den, then the warriors, the leader, and the elders at the end of the circle. That puts the kits and elders closest to the lowest-hanging branches and leaves the warriors facing the entrance, in case of trouble.

The medicine cat's den is in that far corner, beyond the leader's den. Littlecloud found a place where the branches aren't so bunched together—he needs to see the sky so he can read the signs from our warrior ancestors.

Blackstar makes his announcements from the branch that hangs over his den. You should see him swarm up that tree when he's angry!

So that's our camp. I'd let you poke your nose into the dens, but ShadowClan cats aren't friendly to strangers. Even though Blackstar said it would be okay, I think you should keep your stay as short as possible. And if I were you, I wouldn't linger on ShadowClan territory. Head this way, cross a stream, and you'll hit ThunderClan's part of the forest. You'll be perfectly safe there. They take in strays all the time, those softhearted geese.

Bye now!

shADOWCLAN LAke
TERRITORY

(1) ShadowClan camp: Much closer to Twolegs than forest home, but the camp is still well hidden and should be difficult for enemies to attack.

(2) Twoleg nest: Home to two aggressive kittypets. Don't let them catch you out alone, or you're kittypet food!

(3) Twoleg path: Steer clear of these during greenleaf. Twolegs tramp up and down these paths all season long!

(4) Greenleaf Twolegplace: Another place haunted throughout greenleaf by Twolegs, who put up small dens and build terrifying little fires here. On the plus side, sometimes they leave behind food like we used to find at Carrionplace.

RIVERCLAN LAKE CAMP

I know I'm biased—but RiverClan found the best lake home. Have you seen our camp? I'm Mistyfoot, by the way, the RiverClan deputy.

Before we go in, just look around you. The trees are lush, and the stream is full of fish. Back there is the lake. It's harder to catch fish in the lake than it was in the river, but we're learning. The biggest problem is the Twolegs. They love this place in greenleaf!

See where the smaller stream joins the main one? On the triangle of land between the streams is our camp. Can you swim across the stream like a RiverClan cat? Or will you splash through the shallows? You can also jump across on these pebble islands. Watch your step! Some of them are slippery!

Well done. You've made it. Now, look at all the vegetation! You can barely hear the noise of the Twolegs on the lake. See those

brambles? That is the nursery. Quite often there is a patch of sunshine outside the entrance. In those thickets are the dens of the elders and Leopardstar.

Smell that? Sort of sharp and sweet at the same time? That's how you know we're near the medicine cat's den. Come around this thornbush—watch out for the prickles. See how it overhangs the stream? The earth below was washed away, leaving a pool in the roots and a hole in the bank where Mothwing keeps her supplies. She sleeps on that mossy nest. Oh, hello, Willowpaw!

Organizing berries, I see. Is Mothwing with Dawnflower? She was complaining of bellyache this morning. We'll just poke our heads in, take a sniff, and then leave you in peace.

One day this place will be as beautiful as our old camp. We haven't found as many shells in the water, but the Twolegs leave a lot of shiny things behind that our kits like to play with. We check everything carefully before we bring it into the camp, though. So many Twoleg things are bad for us!

Well, that's our camp. Watch your paws crossing the stream, and keep an eye out for Twolegs!

RIVERCLAN LAKE TERRITORY

(1) **RiverClan camp:** Safely tucked away on a triangle of land between two streams, this camp is well sheltered from weather and enemy attack, with easy access to a constant source of prey.

(2) **Greenleaf Twolegplace:** A bees' nest of Twoleg activity during greenleaf! Twoleg kits jump into the lake with loud splashes and shrieks. Some of them can swim like RiverClan cats but more noisily.

(3) **Halfbridge:** A most peculiar bridge that ends halfway out in the water. It doesn't seem to go anywhere! Twolegs tie their "boats" to it.

WINDCLAN LAKE CAMP

Can't you keep up? It must be true what they say about WindClan cats being faster than other cats! Come on, hurry!

Now, rest here and look down. See where my tail is pointing? That's our camp. It doesn't look protected, does it? You don't see any trees or rocks around it. But don't get any ideas! See how many heads are lifted down there? Half the warriors in our camp are watching you, sharpening their claws. No cat comes over these hills without being seen!

You might as well know that I'm Crowfeather and I brought WindClan to this place.

Let's go. Quickly! Follow me down—if you can keep up!

Now you are inside. Keep quiet and look only where I tell you.

This giant boulder is Tallrock, where Onestar makes his speeches. Yes, I know there are plenty of other boulders, but this is the biggest. Stop asking mouse-brained questions! Stop asking *any* questions!

This gorse bush against the boulder is the nursery. Move along—you'll scare the kits! Now, see this boulder? See the large crack in it? Smells like mouse bile, doesn't it? Our medicine cat, Barkface, is treating a tick problem in the camp. WindClan cats must have picked them up on the journey—all that hanging around among trees and swamps. Blech! Anyway, Barkface keeps his supplies in here. Any sick cat can sleep there too. If you ask me, fresh air is the best medicine. But what do I know?

See the tunnel under this gorse bush in the corner? It leads to an old badger set. You wouldn't catch me sleeping inside. It still stinks of badger. I sleep under the sky, near my warrior ancestors. Don't stick your nose in there! Rushtail might claw it off. It's the elders' den now.

So, that's the camp. You can tell Onestar I did as he asked. Now leave! Head straight up the hill and keep going until you see a bunch of large galumphing creatures with hooves. Horses, they're called. Past there is RiverClan territory—maybe they'll share their secrets with you next.

And remember . . . I'll be watching you go!

WINDCLAN LAKE TERRITORY

(1) Moonpool stream: This tumbling stream leads along the edge of the WindClan border and up into the hills to the Moonpool

(2) WindClan camp: A shallow scoop in the ground, open to the sky. Unlike other cats, WindClan warriors prefer to sleep out in the open; in really bad weather, they retreat into underground burrows left by foxes and badgers.

(3) Horseplace: Hear that thundering? It's the pounding of horses' hooves! Stay on this side of the fence!

SkyClan's Territory

SKYROCK

LEAD
DEN

SKY'S
DEN

TWOLEGPLACE

THUNDERPATH

WARRIORS'
DEN

DERS'
EN

NURSERY

MEDICINE
CAT'S DEN

APPRENTICES'
DEN

FALLEN TREE

KPILE

RIVER

TO THE
FOREST →

THE GORGE

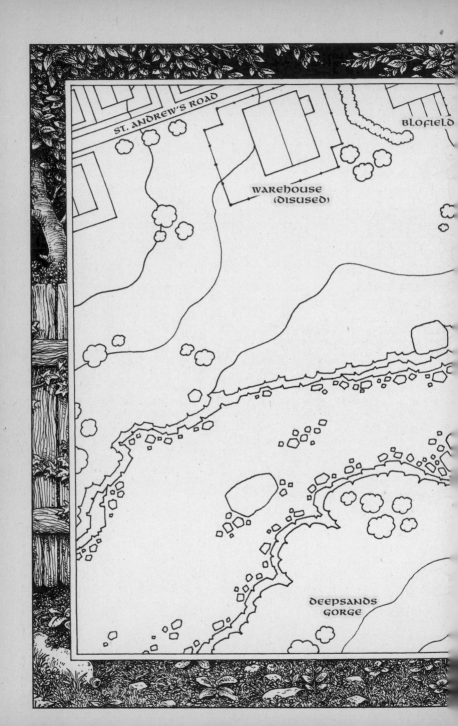

ST. ANDREW'S ROAD

BLOFIELD

WAREHOUSE
(DISUSED)

DEEPSANDS
GORGE

Tour of the Battlefields

THE FOREST
TERRITORIES

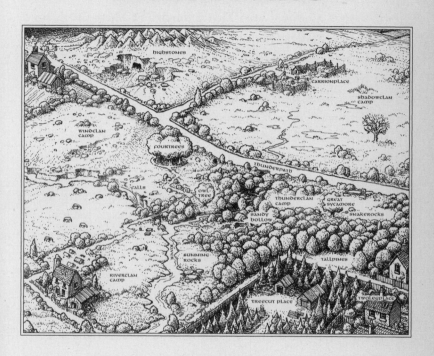

ello, kittypets. You're a long way from home, aren't you? Do you know who I am? I'm sure that you've heard my name, even though no cat would expect you to meet me. I am Tigerstar, once warrior of ThunderClan, then leader of ShadowClan. Now

I walk in the Place of No Stars, the Dark Forest where cats with courage and ambition and cunning are sent, denied entry to StarClan by cats who see no farther than the end of their own noses.

That rustling noise? It's the branches of the four Great Oaks, one for each of the Clans. Look up; can you see them? Yes, we are in the forest, as it once was. This is the hollow where the Clans gathered every full moon—and it's the place where I lost every one of my nine lives, ripped from my belly by that traitor Scourge. Not long after, the Clans fought their greatest battle against Scourge and his followers, who called themselves BloodClan. I should have fought alongside my Clanmates! Instead I could do nothing but watch as the cat who had promised to help me take over the forest waged war against the Clans. They lined up at sunrise here, under the trees looking down into the hollow. Firestar led out the Clans from the other side of the hollow. Can you imagine how puny they looked? If you'd been standing here beside Scourge, you would have had dog claws fitted over your own, and the scent of blood and victory in your throat. You'd just seen your leader kill *me*, the greatest warrior of all the forest Clans; the other warriors must have looked like easy prey.

Just by this rock is where Whitestorm, the ThunderClan deputy, was killed by the BloodClan cat Bone. ThunderClan apprentices avenged his death, jumping onto Bone and dragging him down, clawing the life out of him. Even in the Place of No Stars I could hear his screams, and their shrieks of victory. StarClan never would have let Scourge win that battle. And Firestar showed great courage; I'll grant him that. He'll need every last whisker of it when we meet again.

Are you shivering from cold or are you scared? Stand close to me—it's all right, I bite only my enemies. It's colder now because we're on the open moorland, where WindClan used to live. Looks like their territory by the lake, doesn't it? You can see why they're so skinny and fast, when they have to chase rabbits all the time. Foolish cats, they should learn to stalk and pounce; then they could find fresh-kill under cover of trees. Come to the edge of the camp, in this shallow dip. Can you believe they chose to make their dens here? No wonder ShadowClan forced them out. Brokenstar defeated them with a single patrol, rushing down into the hollow and trapping the WindClan warriors in their nests before they realized what was happening. It was a classic ShadowClan ambush—but in the enemy's own den. Tallstar didn't bring WindClan back to the moor until Firestar and Graystripe fetched him. Firestar has been criticized a lot for constantly interfering in WindClan's affairs, but if Tallstar hadn't shown such weakness against Brokenstar, his Clan never would have gotten so reliant on ThunderClan's help.

Jump! Come on, just one more leap and you'll be on top of Sunningrocks. Look at the view! You can see the whole forest from here; those dark trees in the distance are where ShadowClan lived, and the harsh orange lights over there come from Twolegplace.

Feels peaceful up here, doesn't it? But these rocks have been the site of more battles than anywhere else in the forest. RiverClan would never accept that Sunningrocks belonged to ThunderClan. As if those fat, lazy fox-hearts didn't have enough places to lie in the sun. It's not like they could catch prey on the rocks, since they wouldn't know what to do with a mouse if one sat on their paws. Battles here were *boring*. Whichever cats had the highest place on the rock would win, simple as that. You can't escape when warriors are dropping like rain on your shoulders.

But there was one battle, not long before Firestar joined the Clan, where these rocks served me well. See that gully down there?

Ah, that's better; now we can walk through it. Squeeze past the rock shaped like a cat's muzzle. Here, in this space so narrow that it's almost like a cave, I watched my deputy, Redtail, kill Oakheart, the RiverClan deputy. It was a quick fight—Oakheart tried to use his weight to knock Redtail against the stone wall, but Redtail sprang right over him, reaching down to slice Oakheart's flanks with his claws. Oakheart staggered and crashed onto his knees; he tried to lash out at Redtail, who just stepped backward, knowing the fight was over as Oakheart's life spilled out onto the sand. In that moment, I saw the best opportunity I'd had to make deputy. I was a good warrior; I *deserved* to be deputy. Only Redtail stood in my way.

Look up; see how tight the gully is above our heads. I knew that no cats elsewhere on Sunningrocks would have seen what just happened. The truth about Oakheart's death could die with Redtail. My Clanmate thought I was going to congratulate him. He never saw the strike that fell across his neck. He lay where you're standing now with the light of victory still in his eyes. I carried his body back to the camp and told Bluestar that Oakheart had killed him, and I had taken Oakheart's life in furious vengeance. I should have been made deputy! Not Lionheart! Bluestar knew nothing of justice and true courage!

I had my revenge seasons later, when I became leader of ShadowClan. Dogs came to the forest, fierce and wild and ravenous, and I turned them on my former Clanmates to show they should never have doubted my loyalty. Look around—we're not at Sunningrocks now. This is Snakerocks, a place where few hunting patrols come because of the adders that live here. But ThunderClan had far more to fear when the dogs made a den in a cave under that overhanging slab of rock. I kept the dogs here by bringing them fresh rabbits; it was easy to sneak into ThunderClan's territory when my scent was not fully ShadowClan. The first victims were apprentices, Brightpaw and Swiftpaw, who were foolish enough to hunt too close. Swiftpaw was killed at once; Brightpaw survived, but she has probably wished more than once since then that she hadn't. Did you see her in ThunderClan? The cat with half a face?

If I'd had my way, the dogs would have invaded the ravine, lured there by my trail of rabbits, and destroyed ThunderClan forever. I misjudged the courage of my old Clanmates; I should have known they'd treat this as one more battle, protected by their faith in their precious StarClan. Firestar, who was deputy by then, arranged a line of cats to lead the dogs away from the camp.

We're at the top of the ravine now—look down there, where the bushes are thickest. Our dens were hidden around a clearing; if the dogs had made it that far, the cats would have been trapped by the brambles they had relied on for shelter and protection. Ashfur and Ferncloud ran first, because they had lost their mother, Brindleface, to the dogs. They raced through the trees with the dogs on their heels; then Sandstorm took over. One by one, ThunderClan warriors led the dogs through the trees to the gorge. Do you hear that sound like thunder? That's the river churning along the foot of the cliffs at the edge of WindClan's territory. Bluestar gave up her ninth life to lure the dogs over. In our final battle, she won. She saved her Clan and secured her place in StarClan.

Stay away from the edge! You don't want to follow Bluestar, do you? I have no regrets—everything is turning out as I planned—but I miss those days in the forest, when battles answered all the questions, and my allies would shed every last drop of blood fighting alongside me.

THE LAKE
TERRITORIES

hello! My name is Tawnypelt. I'm a ShadowClan warrior. Did you sleep well? Your fur seems a little ruffled. I expect the sound of the wind might have disturbed you during the night. Onestar has asked me to show you the places where battles have been fought since we moved to the lake. We'll start here, on the moor. Did Onestar tell you that he had to fight for his own leadership as soon as Tallstar died? Every cat expected Mudclaw to take Tallstar's place because he was the WindClan deputy, but on the night Tallstar lost his ninth life, he changed his mind. No cat knows why—only Firestar and Brambleclaw were with him at the time—but he appointed Onewhisker deputy instead. Which meant that by dawn, he was leader of WindClan.

Mudclaw was furious—and can you blame him, really? He'd done nothing wrong. But as a warrior, he should have respected his leader's decision and supported Onestar. Instead, he plotted to take over WindClan by force, and visited all the other Clans in secret, gaining allies. They struck one night, Mudclaw and a RiverClan warrior named Hawkfrost leading the attack. The rest of us fought on Onestar's behalf, and Onestar won—helped by StarClan. Do you see that island down there? With the tall trees? If you look closely, you can make out a fallen tree joining the island to the shore, with its roots on the island side. StarClan sent a bolt of lightning to strike that tree and make it fall on top of Mudclaw, killing him instantly, and showing that Onestar was the true leader of WindClan.

Come this way, along the shore toward ThunderClan's territory. Every cat has the right to walk within three tail-lengths of the water all the way around the lake. If you look through the trees, you might just catch a glimpse of a Twoleg nest. It's falling down now, but there's an old Thunderpath that leads to it, and beyond to the hollow where ThunderClan cats live. The biggest battle since we came to the lake took place here. It started with a border dispute between WindClan and ThunderClan; then the other Clans got involved, and we fought for three days. ShadowClan fought on the side of ThunderClan—that's an alliance that hasn't happened very often!

It was terrible, fighting cats who I'd shared tongues with at Gatherings, or fought alongside in other battles. But that's what being a warrior is all about—being ready to fight for your Clan whenever you have to. You just have to focus on your battle skills, think about what will be achieved or saved by winning, and get on with it. Some cats enjoy it; others see it as their duty.

We're getting close to the ShadowClan border now. Before we cross it, follow me down to the edge of the lake. There isn't a path, but we can walk along this gully. If you duck under that fern, you'll be able to stand on a strip of pebbles right beside the water. It's a great view of the lake, but that's not why I've brought you to this part of the shore. One cat who enjoyed battles too much, in my opinion, died here. So much blood flowed out of him that the lake turned red. The prophecy came true: "Before all is peaceful, blood will spill blood, and the lake will run red." It's okay; you don't need to look so horrified that your paws got a bit wet from that wave. The blood's all washed away now.

The dead cat's name was Hawkfrost, and if you must know, my brother Brambleclaw killed him, to save Firestar's life.

Now, hurry up and we'll go to ShadowClan's territory. Can you walk a bit faster than that? We don't want to get spotted by Twolegs while we're crossing this stretch of grass. ShadowClan and ThunderClan fought over this not long ago; sometimes I think I can still smell blood in the air. Firestar gave us this strip of territory soon after we came to the lake, then changed his mind and demanded it back. As if we'd give it up without a fight! The battle ended when Lionblaze killed Russetfur, our deputy. Warriors should never kill one another for the sake of victory. Neither side won that day.

Most battles are settled more easily, thank StarClan. There were some kittypets living here when we arrived who learned to respect us the hard way. They kept stealing our prey, invading our camp, even lying in wait for our apprentices. Stupid mouse-brains, did they really think they could take on the whole of ShadowClan? We took the battle to their own territory, a Twoleg nest in the middle of the trees, just beyond that rise. They fought well, for pampered kittypets, but they were never going to win.

The kittypets keep out of our way now, but we don't trust them, and our hunting patrols stay away from the Twoleg nest. There are plenty of other places to find prey. No, not here, there's no cover. See how the trees finish and hard black stone covers the ground? This is where Twolegs come in greenleaf to float on the lake. On the far side, where those bushes are, is the start of RiverClan's territory. They've fought their own battle there, against young Twolegs who tried to take over their camp. I heard the warriors made the river wider to protect their dens! Only RiverClan would fight back with water.

It was the same in the old territories, before we came to the lake. You've heard the Clans used to live somewhere else, right? Back then, RiverClan's camp was on the bank of a river, too broad to jump across except in the driest greenleaf. All the fighting was done on the other side of the river, where the rest of the Clans lived. Our territories there weren't so different from the ones we have now—WindClan lived on a moor, ThunderClan among the thickest trees, and ShadowClan in a copse of pines, surrounded by marshland. It's all gone now, crushed and splintered into the mud by Twolegs. All those battles that were fought, the borders we once defended with our lives, the dens where warriors were born and trained, have been lost forever. Good memories as well as bad, fading in the sunlight like dew.

Great StarClan, where did all this mist come from? I'd better get you back to WindClan's camp before we get lost. Come on, follow me.

FIGHTING TECHNIQUES

One of the most important skills a mentor must teach an apprentice is how to fight. Warriors are often called upon to defend the borders or protect the Clan from attack, whether by enemy Clans or predators like badgers and foxes. Even medicine cats must learn enough fighting technique to be useful in battle.

Back kick Explosive surprise move to catch opponent from behind. Judge opponent's distance from you carefully; then lash out with your back legs, taking your weight on your front paws.

Belly rake A fight-stopper. Slice with unsheathed claws across soft flesh of opponent's belly. If you're pinned down, the belly rake quickly puts you back in control.

Front paw blow Frontal attack. Bring your front paw down hard on your opponent's head. Claws sheathed.

Front paw strike Frontal attack. Slice downward with your front paw at the body or face of your opponent. Claws unsheathed.

Killing bite A death blow to the back of the neck. Quick and silent and sometimes considered dishonorable. Used only as a last resort.

Leap-and-hold Ideal for a small cat facing a large opponent. Spring onto opponent's back and grip with unsheathed claws. Now you are beyond the range of your opponent's paws and in position to inflict severe body wounds. A group of apprentices can defeat a large and danger-ous warrior in this way. It was deployed to great effect against BloodClan's deputy, Bone. Watch for the drop-and-roll countermove, and try to jump free before you get squashed.

Partner fighting Warriors who have trained and fought together will often instinctively fall into a paired defensive position, each protecting the other's back while fending off an opponent on either side. Slashing, clawing, and leaping together, battle pairs can be a whirlwind of danger for attackers.

Play dead Effective in a tight situation, such as when you are pinned. Stop struggling and go limp. When your opponent relaxes his grip, thinking you are defeated, push yourself up explosively. This will throw off an unwary opponent and put you in an attacking position.

Scruff shake Secure a strong teeth grip in the scruff of your opponent's neck; then shake violently until he or she is too rattled to fight back. Most effective against rats, which are small enough to throw. A strong throw will stun or kill them.

Teeth grip Target your opponent's extremities—the legs, tail, scruff, or ears—and sink in your teeth and hold. This move is similar to the leap-and-hold except your claws remain free to fight.

Upright lock Final, crushing move on already weakened opponent. Rear up on back legs and bring full weight down on opponent. If opponent does same, wrestle and flip him under you. This move makes you vulnerable to the belly rake, so requires great strength and speed.

GLOSSARY

Catspeak: Humanspeak

Crow-food: rotting food

Fox dung: an insult; stronger offense than mouse-brain

Fresh-kill: recently killed prey

Gathering: a meeting that the Clans hold in peace at every full moon

Greencough: severe chest infection, which can be fatal in elders and young kits

Greenleaf: summer

Greenleaf Twolegplace: a place where humans visit only in the summer (a campsite, resort, etc.)

Halfbridge: a dock

Horseplace: fields and stables near the lake where half-tamed cats live

Housefolk: a house cat's word for its humans

Kittypet: a house cat

Leaf-bare: winter

Leaf-fall: fall/autumn

Loner: cat that lives peacefully on its own in one place but doesn't defend its territory

Monster: usually refers to human machines such as cars and bulldozers

Moonhigh: the time of night when the moon is at its highest—often midnight

Mouse-brained: not very smart

Mouse dung: an insult; stronger than mouse-brain, but less offensive than fox dung

Newleaf: spring

Nofurs: another word for humans

One moon: one month (half-moon = two weeks, quarter-moon = one week)

Rogue: a potentially hostile cat who lives outside the Clans and never spends too long in one place

Sharing tongues: term used to describe cats grooming each other

Silverpelt: the Milky Way

Sun-drown-place: the sea to the west, where the sun sets

Sunhigh: noon

Thunderpath: a road

Tree-eater: bulldozer

Twoleg nest: a human house

Twolegplace: a human town

Twolegs: the Clans' word for humans

Upwalkers: another word for humans

Whitecough: mild chest infection

Chapter One:
Welcome, Warrior!

Welcome to the *Warriors Adventure Game!*

In this game, you and your friends will create cat characters of your own and lead them through exciting adventures. Along the way, your characters may bump into familiar faces, and visit some of the same places as the warrior cats. You'll also meet new characters and experience adventures no warrior cat has ever dreamed of. What's more, you won't just read about these situations; you will control what your characters do and how the problems they face get resolved.

What Is an Adventure Game?

In an adventure game, you and your friends each will create a character in a story—in this case, cats from the warrior Clans. Your cats will find themselves involved in adventures and mysteries, just like the characters in the novels.

At its heart the *Warriors Adventure Game* is a kind of group storytelling event. As a group, you and your friends will create tales about your cats' adventures. You get to decide what your character thinks and says and does based on what his or her individual goals are. While you'll keep track of different scores, the game itself mostly involves talking about and imagining what your cat characters would do in certain situations.

Are There Rules?

Like any game, this one has rules. Some of them are rules about how to create your cat, while others are about how to tell whether or not your cat is successful at the things he or she tries to do.

At first glance it might seem as if there are an awful lot of rules—so many that it may be a bit intimidating. Don't worry. First of all, you don't have to learn every rule to play. There are just a few basic rules that you'll need during most of the game. The rest of them will only come up in certain situations.

Secondly, and best of all, you can always look up the rules when they do come into play. There is no need for you to memorize anything.

The *Warriors Adventure Game* is a cooperative game. You and your friends work together to tell your characters' tales. Storytelling is the most basic action in this game, and the only thing you ever really need to know is the answer to one simple question: What would your cat do next?

Who Wins?

There are no winners and losers in the *Warriors Adventure Game*. The goal is not to win or beat the other players; the goal is to have a good time playing and to successfully complete each adventure.

In fact, you can consider Rule #1 to be:

Having fun is more important than following the rules as written.

That's not to say that you should just throw out these rules. They have been designed to help make the game more fun for everyone involved. However, because a storytelling game has almost limitless possibilities, there may be times where following the rules leads to confusion or even arguments. At those times remember Rule #1.

As long as everyone playing the game is having fun, then you're definitely doing it right.

What You'll Need

The best way to learn the *Warriors Adventure Game* is to jump right in and make a cat character for yourself. It will get you familiar with the rules and will teach you a lot about what the game will be like. In order to do that and begin playing, you'll need the following things.

These Rules: Since you're reading this sentence, you've already got your first need covered.

Paper and Pencil: Making your cat character is really just a matter of making a few simple choices and jotting down the results. But as you're creating your cat for the first time, you might also want to write down questions as they occur to you. Most of them will be answered as you go through the character creation process; but if you write them down, you and your friends can sort them out later. It's also handy to keep a paper and pencil around while you're playing. As the story unfolds, you may want to jot down important information or make other notes to yourself.

Character Sheet: A character sheet is a page designed to hold all the information you'll need about your character during the course of play. Chapters Two and Three will walk you through the process of making a character. Download and print one out at www.warriorcats.com or make a copy of someone else's. When you're finished creating your cat, all the information you'll need to play will be on that one sheet.

Imagination: This really is the most important thing every player must bring to the table. The whole premise of the *Warriors Adventure Game* is that you and your friends are able to imagine your cats, their personalities, and the world around them.

That's It for Now: Eventually, you'll need a few more items—in particular, you'll need three different kinds of chips (colored stones, coins, etc.)—but not until you start playing the game. During the game you may also find it useful to keep a map of the Lake region handy so you can track where your cats are going. A full-color copy of the map has been specially made for the game (you can find it on the reverse side of the jacket for *Omen of the Stars #1: The Fourth Apprentice*, or as a download on warriorcats.com). For now, though, as long as you have the items listed above, you're ready to create a cat.

What Makes a Warrior?

Before you go to the next chapter and start creating your cat, let's take a quick look at what the end result will be—an apprentice cat's character sheet. Below is the character sheet for a cat that we've created: Muddypaw, a young apprentice from WindClan. You'll learn more about Muddypaw as we go along through these rules, and we'll watch him develop at the same time your cat does.

Muddypaw

Although Muddypaw wants to help his Clan, fighting makes him nervous. He's physically small, but he's very clever and makes friends easily.

If you'd like, you can draw a picture of your cat as you imagine him or her. Here's a picture of Muddypaw, the cat we'll be playing with as we go through the rules.

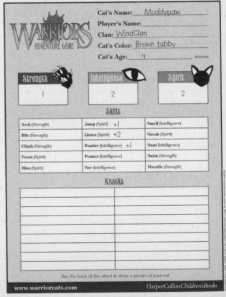

Cat's Name: Muddypaw
Player's Name:
Clan: WindClan
Cat's Color: Brown tabby
Cat's Age: 4 moons

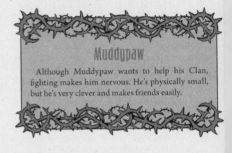

Strength	Intelligence	Spirit
1	2	2

Skills

Arch (Strength)	Jump (Spirit) +1	Smell (Intelligence)
Bite (Strength)	Listen (Spirit) +2	Sneak (Spirit)
Climb (Strength)	Ponder (Intelligence) +1	Swat (Intelligence)
Focus (Spirit)	Pounce (Intelligence)	Swim (Strength)
Hiss (Spirit)	See (Intelligence)	Wrestle (Strength)

Knacks

Use the back of this sheet to draw a picture of your cat.

How the Game Works

While Muddypaw's character sheet does not have an overwhelming amount of information, it still can look a little confusing. What do all those numbers mean? Before we go any further, let's take a quick look at how those numbers will be used in play. This will give you a basic idea of what playing the *Warriors Adventure Game* will be like.

In this example, Erica and Bill are playing a short session of the *Warriors Adventure Game*. Bill is the Narrator, and he has an adventure printed out and sitting in front of him on the table. Erica is playing. Her character is Muddypaw, so she has the character sheet you just saw printed out and sitting in front of her. She also has one red chip, two blue chips, and two green chips. These chips are based on Muddypaw's Ability scores: the red chip is for the one Strength point, blue for Intelligence, and green for Spirit. (When you play, the chips can be any colors you like as long as they are easy to tell apart.)

Bill: Muddypaw's training assignment today is to go out alone and catch some fresh-kill for the Clan. So where do you go after you leave the WindClan camp?

Erica: I'm not sure. Where would be a good place to hunt?

Bill: To figure that out, you'll have to make a Ponder Check.

Erica: Ponder—that Skill is based on Intelligence, right?

Bill: Right.

Erica: Okay. Muddypaw has a score of 2 in Intelligence.

Bill: And is he trained in the Ponder Skill?

Erica: Yeah. He has a +1 in Ponder. So 2 plus 1 is 3.

Bill: So you have a Ponder Check of 3.

Bill looks at the adventure to see what that result means.

Bill: Okay, you remember a spot where there are a lot of vole burrows.

Erica: Voles? They're easy to catch! Muddypaw is going there!

Bill: Okay. You get there. Now make a See Check to find out if you can see any voles running around.

Erica: That's also based on Intelligence, but I don't have any training in the See Skill. So I just get a 2 from my Intelligence score.

Bill: With a See Check of 2, you don't notice anything.

Erica: How about if I try to hear the voles scurrying around?

Bill: That's a good idea. Make a Listen Check.

Erica: Listen is also based on Spirit, but I AM trained in it. In fact, Muddypaw gets +2 to Listen Checks becurse he's from WindClan, so my total is 4. But I really want to listen hard, so I'm going to spend one of my green chips to get a bonus point.

Erica takes a green chip and sets it aside.

Erica: That gives me 1 bonus point, so my total is 5.

Bill: Great! With a 5 you definitely hear the voles. They're scurrying all around here, and you can tell that one is right near you!

Erica: I want to get it!

Bill: How do you want to do that?

Erica: Well, I'm hunting, so I want to chomp on it.

Bill: Doing that requires a Bite Check. That's based on Strength.

Erica: Oh. Muddypaw's Strength is only 1, and he's not trained in Bite.

Bill: Sorry, a 1 isn't good enough. You miss and the vole scurries away. But you hear another one nearby.

Erica: This time I'm going to get it. I'm going to spend my Strength chip.

Erica takes the red chip and sets it aside.

Erica: That gives me 1 bonus point to my Strength Check, so the total is now 2.

Bill: That's still not very high, but it's enough to get the vole. Now figure out how much damage you do.

Erica: Okay, Muddypaw's Strength is 1, so he's only going to do 1 point of damage . . . but I do get an extra +1 because he's biting. That's a total of 2.

Bill: More than enough to kill a vole.

Erica: Great! I can't wait to add my vole to the fresh-kill pile!

Bill: But one vole won't feed many cats. What are you going to do now?

Erica: Hunt some more, of course!

As the game continues, Bill will use the adventure to describe more things that happen to Muddypaw, and Erica will continue to tell him how her cat reacts. That's pretty much how every session of the *Warriors Adventure Game* will go, except that you'll be playing with a group of friends who each have a cat character, and you'll all be making the decisions together. The adventures your cats go on will be more detailed than just hunting for voles, but the basics of the game will remain the same.

Just the Beginning

Now that you know what a character sheet in the *Warriors Adventure Game* looks like and have a basic idea of how the game mechanics work, it's time for you to begin creating your own cat character.

In Chapter Two you will pull together the basic information that defines your cat as he or she starts down the road to being a warrior. You will create your cat as an apprentice just entering training. When you're done with this first part of creating your cat, you'll have a character that is in the same stage of life as Muddypaw.

Chapter Three will allow you to give your cat the full advantage of warrior training and you will begin to decide what aspects of the warrior's life are most important to him or her—that will put the finishing touches on your character sheet.

In Chapter Seven you will find character sheets for a few of the important cats from the Warriors books, and Chapter Eight has a mini-adventure so that you and your friends can jump right in and begin playing the game. If you are anxious to start playing right away, you and your friends can each select a character from Chapter Seven and use him or her to play the adventure in Chapter Eight, then create your own cat characters afterward. But we recommend taking the time to create your own cat first. It's a fun process, and it will help you understand the game better.

Chapter Two: Creating Your Cat

Every cat, from the strongest warrior to the most spoiled kittypet, begins his or her Clan training as an apprentice. The same is true for your character in the *Warriors Adventure Game*, so your first step will be to figure out what your cat is like at the beginning of his or her training.

Part of this creation process is pure imagination. You get to picture what kind of cat your character is at heart: What things does he love? What does she hope to achieve for herself and her Clan? What makes him lose his temper? What's her favorite thing to do on a sunny summer afternoon?

With those ideas in mind, you will make a few simple choices and create the core of your game character. In Chapter Three you will build on that core character as your apprentice graduates to being a full-fledged warrior. This is still just the beginning of his or her life story, though. As you play through adventures, your cat will continue to grow and improve.

Character Sheet

You can download blank character sheets from the warriorcats.com website. If you can, print one out now and keep it handy as you go through the next few chapters. If not, don't worry. You can write down all of this information in a notebook or on a piece of scrap paper, then transfer the results to a character sheet later.

Who Are You?

The apprentice you're creating will be your alter ego in the adventures you're about to undertake, so it's important that you understand him or her inside and out. Begin by thinking about the following questions. You don't need firm answers to them all, but having general ideas about them will help you make some of the decisions you'll have to make during this character creation process and during the course of play. They will help you understand who your cat is, what he or she thinks is important, and what he or she will do in stressful situations.

You don't have to write down the answers. They are not important to the game except that they will help you to understand who your cat is. Just remember to think about these questions from the apprentice's perspective, not your own real-world point of view.

- Which is more important, being strong or smart?
- When out on patrol, would you rather be alone in the front or part of the main group?
- Do you enjoy listening to the elders tell stories about what happened many moons ago?
- Would you rather be the Clan's deputy or its medicine cat?
- Which is more important, to know how to do something or to understand why it should be done?
- If you saw a rogue cat in your territory, would you chase it off yourself or go tell the rest of the Clan?

Start by Talking

There are many different types of cats in the Warriors books, with a wide variety of personalities and goals. Just imagine how boring the stories would be if *every* cat had exactly the same skills, abilities, problems, and dreams. It is the mix of bravery, fear, hope, strength, weakness, ambition, and a thousand other emotions, goals, and motivations that make the Warriors world so engaging.

The same will be true in the *Warriors Adventure Game*. It may be a good idea to sit down with the other people with whom you'll be playing the game and talk about what kinds of cats you all hope to build. If everyone builds a nearly identical character, the game will be a little boring and probably too competitive. Players may feel the need to prove that their cat is the best of the lot. And if the cats come across a problem that none of them is well suited to deal with, how will the group succeed?

On the other hand, if the characters have a fairly wide array of Skills and Abilities, and a healthy mix of outlooks on life, the group will be much better able to handle a variety of different stories and situations.

- Is a sharp sense of smell more important for hunting or for knowing when an enemy is near?
- Would you rather be a good climber or a good swimmer?
- Which is worse, being hungry or being cold?
- Does StarClan ever send you dreams?
- If an enemy was attacking your camp, would you rather be defending the main entrance or guarding the weak sections of the walls?
- Which is scarier, a dog or a snake?

At this point you should have a fairly strong idea of who your cat is and what kind of warrior he or she hopes to grow up to be. In just one or two sentences, write down a basic description of your cat's personality and goals.

For example: *Muddypaw is quiet and a little shy, but he's fiercely loyal to his friends and his Clan. Fighting makes him nervous, and he hopes to one day become a great medicine cat.*

Once you are satisfied with your description, it's time to choose a Clan and decide your cat's Ability scores.

Choosing a Clan

As anyone who has read the Warriors novels knows, cats don't choose their Clans—they're born into them. But things are a little more forgiving in the *Warriors Adventure Game*. You get to choose which Clan your apprentice belongs to, and your decision will be one of the first things other players look to when assessing your cat and deciding how to approach him or her.

Chances are, you already know a good deal about the four Clans that live around the Lake, but a basic description of each is provided below. First, though, let's talk about a few points you may want to consider before selecting your cat's Clan.

Other Players

The *Warriors Adventure Game* is a cooperative experience. It might be a good idea to sit down and talk to the other players about their expectations for what the game will be like. If everyone else wants to be members of a single Clan, then it might be difficult if you decide to play a cat that is antagonistic toward that Clan.

Even if everyone wants to play cats from different Clans, there may be some tension. What if half of the players want their cats to be open and cooperative with other Clans, but the other half want to be suspicious and aggressive?

Remember, It's Just a Game

A lot is said in this chapter about the importance of personalizing your character, understanding who he or she is, and creating a strong mental bond with him or her. This is to help you get into the spirit of role-playing your character, but remember: when all is said and done, this is only a game and the apprentice you are creating is not real. Just as in the Warriors novels, a lot of bad things can happen to your character during the course of his or her adventures. He or she can become wounded or worse, but it's all part of the game.

Nothing that happens in the *Warriors Adventure Game* is any more real than your imagination.

None of these problems is insurmountable, but it is important for the group to get together and talk about them before the game begins, and preferably before characters are created.

Other Characters

Once you have an idea how the other players feel about the different Clans, you may want to look at things from those characters' perspective.

If one of the other cats has a dark history with a certain Clan—perhaps having had a relative killed in a battle or having been bullied by members of the Clan at some point—it will make relationships within the group more difficult if your cat comes from that Clan.

Of course, just as this sort of thing can make for good stories, it can also make for good storytelling games. However, you should be clear about that sort of thing *before* starting play.

Clan History

Remember that all of the players will probably be just as familiar with the world of the Warriors novels as you are—perhaps even more so. They will enter the game with ideas about what it means to come from each of the Clans, and those ideas will probably be shared by most of the people in the game.

Sometimes it's fun to imagine a character that goes "against type," for example, a member of ThunderClan who is greedy, covetous, and antagonistic toward the other Clans. However, you should remember that the other players will probably expect your character to fit the usual image of his or her Clan. And if you intend to make your character something different, you should let the other players know right away so there is no confusion.

Personal Storyline

Even within the most close-knit Clan, individual cats have a wide variety of goals and aspirations. However, in the world of the Warriors novels, the Clan almost always comes first. Bear that in mind, particularly if your cat and any of the other characters are from the same Clan. The other players will expect your cat to remain true to the warrior code, and you should expect no less from them.

 ## ThunderClan

While all the Clans enjoy times of peace and relative calm, ThunderClan is probably the Clan that does the most to promote quiet coexistence for all cats. These cats are respectful of other Clans, their habits, and their territories. ThunderClan has a long history of speaking out against injustice and seeking to mediate differences between individual cats and even whole Clans.

While Thunderclan cats believe strongly in living up to both the letter and the intent of the warrior code, they also are not afraid to challenge traditions and laws that seem unfair. ThunderClan is most interested in seeing that all cats are treated with justice and respect.

Some Clans interpret ThunderClan's willingness to compromise as a weakness. They believe that the Clan spends so much time talking about "fairness" because they lack the strength to protect themselves from aggressors. But the members of ThunderClan are more than ready to back up their beliefs with tooth and claw if necessary.

ThunderClan Bonus

Any cat that is a member of ThunderClan automatically has 1 level of training in the Ponder Skill. (Skills will be explained in detail later in this chapter.) When it is time to pick Skills, you may make one of your choices to increase the value of your Ponder Skill from 1 to 2.

 ## RiverClan

Each Clan has many impressive qualities, but members of RiverClan are especially proud of their Clan and its history. Cats in this Clan tend to be sleek and have long, glossy coats.

RiverClan cats are fiercely self-sufficient. Because of their close ties to the water, RiverClan cats are usually excellent swimmers who don't mind being wet the way other cats often do.

Some other Clans think that RiverClan is a little too proud, and that makes it more difficult for them to weather hard times. But the members of RiverClan say that they only do what every other Clan does—use any means necessary to keep themselves strong and healthy.

RiverClan Bonus

Any cat that is a member of RiverClan automatically has 1 level of training in the Swim Skill. When it is time to pick Skills, you may make one of your choices to increase the value of your Swim Skill from 1 to 2.

 ## WindClan

Every Clan suffers through difficult times occasionally, but WindClan has a more troubled history than most. These cats are the most susceptible to extremes of weather and incursions by animals, Twolegs, and even other cats. But in the end they always come back to reclaim what is theirs.

Cats in WindClan must be quick and have extra-sharp senses (particularly hearing) in order to successfully hunt on the open moor. As a result, they are especially difficult to take by surprise.

Some other Clans interpret WindClan's history of coming and going as indicating that these cats are cowardly—running away from threats rather than facing them. They think that living on a barren plain has made them soft, weak, and unfit to be called warriors. But the cats of WindClan will point out that there is no honor to be gained from unnecessary fighting. And no one has ever succeeded in permanently taking territory away from their Clan.

WindClan Bonus

Any cat that is a member of WindClan automatically has 1 level of training in the Listen Skill. When it is time to pick Skills, you may make one of your choices to increase the value of your Listen Skill from 1 to 2.

 ## ShadowClan

All of the Clans value their privacy, but none more so than ShadowClan. Members pride themselves on being the most aggressive and battle-hardened Clan cats, always ready for a fight and never needing to bow their heads or give concessions to anyone. Living in the wildest of territories, they believe that survival of the fittest is a basic part of the warrior code. If a Clan cannot defend its territory against invasion, then that Clan doesn't deserve that land after all. If you're strong, clever, or sneaky enough to get something, then it rightfully belongs to you.

Some Clans interpret ShadowClan's aggression and deception as proof that these cats are nothing more than battle hungry, untrustworthy sneaks. But the cats of ShadowClan believe they have the truest warriors of any Clan, and if anyone wants to contest that claim they'll have to back it up with claws and fury.

ShadowClan Bonus

Any cat that is a member of ShadowClan automatically has 1 level of training in the Sneak Skill. When it is time to pick Skills, you may make one of your choices to increase the value of your Sneak Skill from 1 to 2.

Ability Scores

Ability scores represent your cat's most basic physical, mental, and emotional abilities. Just about everything your character does in the *Warriors Adventure Game* will be based at least partially on his or her Ability scores. And the best part is that over time these numbers will get better as your cat gains experience through adventures.

The three Abilities are: Strength, Intelligence, and Spirit. Each Ability is linked to a specific kind of activity, and is represented by a number between 1 and 10. As an apprentice, your character only has a total of 5 points to spread among these abilities.

After reading the descriptions below, decide what your kit's starting Ability scores will be. He or she *must* have at least 1 point in each Ability. With only 5 points to spend, this limits your possibilities, so choose carefully.

When you've decided just how you want your apprentice's Ability scores to be distributed, write them down on your character sheet.

Strength

Strength represents your apprentice's physical power and coordination. Cats with higher Strength scores are better able to climb, pounce, wrestle, and do other bits of roughhousing. When they fight, Strength makes their blows hit harder (though not necessarily land more accurately).

Cats with the higher Strength scores are usually larger, or at least more muscular, and more imposing than cats with lower Strength scores. They tend to make good warriors and hunters, and are generally admired for providing protection for the Clan.

Muddypaw

You already know what Muddypaw's Ability scores are, but it might be helpful to see why they are that way.

With only 5 points to spend, Muddypaw had to have at least one Ability with a score of 1. Since he is a relatively small cat that doesn't like fighting or roughhousing, we chose to put only 1 point in Strength. That left 4 points to spend on Intelligence and Spirit. Should those points be split evenly— 2 apiece—or should one Ability be clearly better than the others—splitting the points 3 and 1?

This was a tough decision, because both Intelligence and Spirit are important to Muddypaw. He likes to think things through carefully before he acts, but once he's made up his mind about a course of action he is quite determined. After thinking about it for a while, we decided that the two abilities were equally important, so each one got a score of 2.

Choose a high Strength score if your cat wants to be especially good at fighting, hunting, and other physical activities.

 Intelligence

Intelligence represents your cat's general knowledge and ability to figure out solutions to difficult problems. Cats with higher Intelligence scores are better able to remember things they've heard or seen before, figure out ways to successfully deal with new situations, and make complex plans to reach a difficult goal. When they fight, Intelligence lets them make very accurate strikes (though not necessarily land them with any extra power).

Cats with higher Intelligence scores are usually considered to be the cleverest in the Clan and are looked to for leadership in emergencies that require quick reactions. They tend to make good sentries and strategists, and are generally admired for having a keen understanding of the ways of the world. This sort of cat will often grow to be a good candidate for deputy— perhaps one day even a Clan leader.

Choose a high Intelligence score if your apprentice wants to be especially good at tracking, spotting danger, and understanding mysterious events.

Spirit

Spirit represents your cat's general willpower and ability to understand how other cats feel about different situations. Cats with higher Spirit scores are better at resisting the temptations of curiosity, anticipating what someone else will do in a given situation, and sensing unseen changes in the world. When they fight, Spirit lets them anticipate where their foes are likely to strike next and get out of the way (though it doesn't help much when it comes to striking back).

Cats with higher Spirit scores are usually considered very insightful and are often asked for advice on personal matters. They tend to make good leaders and medicine cats, and are generally admired for being able to see through to the heart of any problem.

Choose a high Spirit score if your apprentice wants to be good at understanding the thoughts and problems of other cats, or take on a role of responsibility such as being a medicine cat or a cat who the leader depends on for advice.

How Do I Choose?

Choosing your Ability scores may seem a little daunting at first. With only 5 points to spend, how can you choose where they belong?

As with everything else in the *Warrior Adventure Game*, the answer comes right from your imagination. Just think about your cat and what aspects of life are most important to him or her.

You can choose to have one Ability be significantly better than the other two, but making that choice means your apprentice will be at a disadvantage in the other areas. Alternatively, you can choose to have the scores distributed more evenly, but then your apprentice will not stand out as being excellent in any area.

The thing to remember is, there is no "right" or "wrong" answer. Whatever choices match the personality and goals of the kit you imagined in your mind are the ones to make.

Skills

Not everything a cat does depends solely on his or her innate Strength, Intelligence, and Spirit. If that were true, then the strongest cat would win every fight and the smartest cat could never be misled or outmaneuvered.

In addition to Ability scores, characters in the *Warriors Adventure Game* also have Skills. A Skill is represented by a number between 0 and 5. The higher the number, the more advanced the Skill.

Skills represent particular actions that every cat is able to make but that can be improved by training or practice rather than by relying just on raw natural ability. Each Skill builds on one of the Ability scores (listed in parentheses at the beginning of each of the Skill descriptions). So while two cats might have 5 levels in the Climb Skill, for example, the cat with the higher Strength score would still be the better climber.

Choosing Skills

Apprentices have three Skills at which they are particularly good. Read the Skill descriptions below and then, using the insights you've gained into your cat's personality and goals, select three Skills that he or she would find most useful and mark a 1 next to those on your character sheet.

As your cat gets older and gains experience, you will have the chance to choose new Skills for your cat, or to raise the value of the Skills your cat already has. However, **a Skill can never be increased above a value of 5.**

Just a Starting Point

Remember, the Ability scores and Skills your cat has as an apprentice are only the starting point. None of us begins life being as strong, smart, or wise as we want to be, and there are always opportunities for us to learn and grow.

As your cat gets older and gains experience, you will be given the chance to select new Skills and increase your Ability scores. If you let the questions you answered at the beginning of this chapter guide these decisions, you'll soon find your character is becoming just the cat he or she always dreamed of being.

Arch

(Strength)—This Skill represents a cat's ability to arch its back, strike an aggressive pose, or otherwise look mean and intimidating. This can be used to frighten away an enemy or, more commonly, as a way to show a Clanmate just how serious you are about a subject. A contest of arching is sometimes used by two or more cats who find themselves in a confrontation but want to resolve the matter without actually fighting.

Bite

(Strength)—This is a measure of how much damage a cat can do when Biting an opponent. Because Bites cause so much damage, they are generally only used when hunting for fresh-kill or fighting against wild animals. Even when Clans are in serious battles, warriors usually only fight using Swats and Wrestling. The warrior code makes it clear that Biting is reserved for prey and attacking animals who are outside the warrior code.

Climb

(Strength)—The Climb Skill determines how quickly and skillfully a cat can go up a tree, fence, or other obstacle. It also represents how securely a cat can hang on to a branch, tree trunk, or other perch when the wind or an enemy is trying to shake him or her loose. In most cases, cats do not Climb down objects (their claws are not built for that sort of thing). Instead, they usually use the Jump Skill to get down.

Focus

(Spirit)—There are many distractions in the world, be they strange noises, pain, other cats, Twolegs, or simply boredom. Focus represents a cat's ability to concentrate on a certain task and ignore other distractions. Often, a successful use of the Focus Skill will be required before a cat can use another particularly useful Skill under difficult conditions.

Hiss

(Spirit)—This represents a cat's ability to hiss, yowl, and otherwise give voice to his or her anger and other aggressive feelings. It is often used in conjunction with the Arch Skill but can also be used on its own. Hissing is a way of warning nearby cats of approaching danger, or of telling dogs or other animals that you have no intention of running away and that they should only come closer if they truly want a fight.

Jump

(Spirit)—Jumping has several uses, but all of them are defensive in nature. When a cat is surprised by something that presents some kind of danger, his or her first reaction is to Jump. A cat will also Jump during battle in an effort to avoid an enemy's attacks. As mentioned in the description of the Climb Skill, cats generally use the Jump Skill to get down from high places safely. And, finally, in cases where a cat is knocked off or falls from a high place accidentally, the Jump Skill allows him or her to land safely on all four feet rather than uncontrollably crash to the ground and risk a serious injury.

Listen

(Spirit)—This skill represents two things. First, the Listen Skill is used to tell if a cat notices a certain sound or noise. This is a crucial part of hunting, not to mention noticing the approach of any unexpected visitors (be they other cats, animals, or Twolegs). Second, because cats' ears are so sharp, the Listen Skill can also be used to tell them exactly where a sound is coming from and who or what it is (if the sound is familiar).

Ponder

(Intelligence)—Cats use this Skill to figure out things they have never encountered or been taught before. This can be as straightforward as trying to figure out a way to get past a sleeping dog or over a fence or hedge. It can also be as complex as trying to determine what a new sound or smell means and whether or not it presents a danger. Even when successful, the Ponder Skill only provides a cat with an idea. Making the idea work will often involve some other Skill entirely.

Pounce

(Intelligence)—Pouncing is similar to Jumping but, rather than being defensive in nature, a Pounce is always aggressive or offensive. This Skill is most often used in hunting: to land on and quickly kill prey. However, in a fight a cat may also use it to leap onto an opponent and begin Wrestling. Pounce is also the Skill used when a cat wants to go over or across a space and land on an object without Climbing. A cat can Pounce on something that is up to two body lengths away or above him or her (there is no limit to how far a cat can Pounce downward, but really that's more like falling and may be risky based on the situation).

See

(Intelligence)—This is the Skill used to determine if a cat can notice something using only his or her eyes. Usually this is easier if the thing is moving. See is one of the Skills used during hunting and while patrolling, but because cats also have such sharp senses of hearing and smell, it is not as crucial a Skill as it is for Twolegs. Cats also use their See Skill to tell if anything has changed about a place, thing, or other cat since the last time they encountered it.

Smell

(Intelligence)—There are two common uses for the Smell Skill. First, like the See and Listen Skills, a cat can use the Smell Skill to tell if someone or something else is nearby. Because cats' noses are so sensitive, Smell can identify exactly where the thing is, even if the cat can't see it. In addition, cats can use the Smell Skill to follow the scent trails that all living creatures leave wherever they go. In this way, the Skill can be used to follow someone who passed by hours or possibly even days ago. However, the older a scent trail is, the harder it is to follow.

Sneak

(Spirit)—Many situations call for a cat to move undetected: hunting, moving through another Clan's territory, going past a dog or group of Twolegs. Sneak is the Skill that governs such movements. More than just being quiet or stealthy, the Sneak Skill is a combination of those plus an element of timing and anticipating where your quarry will be looking at any moment.

Swat

(Intelligence)—This is the general-purpose Skill used to see if a cat can hit something with his or her paw. In training and roughhouse play, this is done with claws retracted, but in a fight it is done with claws extended in hopes of causing injury. The difference between an ordinary blow and an especially effective one is not a matter of having a higher Strength score, though; it's one of timing and placement (which is why Swat is an Intelligence-based Skill).

Swim

(Strength)—Although most cats are not fond of the water (except those in RiverClan, of course), being able to Swim long enough to safely reach dry land is definitely a useful Skill. While Swimming is not something a cat is likely to do often, when the need arises, it is handy to have trained in this Skill.

Wrestle

(Strength)—Wrestling is a catch-all phrase for the kind of fighting cats do once they are directly on top of each other and too close to rear back and Swat. It is a good way for a larger cat to immobilize a smaller opponent, and also probably the best way for a smaller cat to hurt a larger opponent (since it brings them close enough to use sharp rear claws or, in extreme cases, even to Bite).

Muddypaw's Skills

You've seen Muddypaw's Skill selections on his character sheet, but let's look at why he made those choices.

Muddypaw is a very deliberate cat. He likes to be certain about his actions before he takes them, so the first Skill he chose was Ponder. That Skill helps when a cat is trying to remember something or puzzle out a mystery.

Next he chose Jump because Muddypaw does not like fighting. Jump is the Skill that cats use to avoid blows in a fight and to get away from dangerous situations.

Finally, Muddypaw chose Listen because he thinks that's the best way to keep track of what's going on around him. Clever enemies can hide or mask their scents, but the whole world makes sounds and if you pay close attention to them you have an advantage over everyone else around you. Of course, as a member of WindClan, Muddypaw automatically gets training in Listen, so rather than a +1 he begins play with a +2 in the Listen Skill.

Ready to Go

You've now determined your cat's basic personality and goals, picked a Clan, assigned his or her Ability scores, and chosen three beginning Skills. Your apprentice is ready to begin training and grow into a warrior that any Clan would be proud of.

Your cat is now at the same stage that Muddypaw was in the example in Chapter One. If you want, you can begin playing the game right now. But things are much tougher for apprentices than they are for warriors. This is a stage when a cat spends just about all of his or her time training, not running around on adventures.

In the next chapter, your cat will get that training, improve his or her Abilities, and learn a few helpful tricks that only experience can impart. And when it's all said and done, your cat will be a full-fledged warrior!

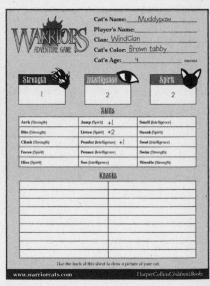

Chapter Three: Grooming a Warrior

Every apprentice looks forward to the day when, after moons of training, he or she is promoted to the full status of a warrior, and is able to participate in all the Clan activities and be responsible for keeping the Clan safe and well fed. During their apprenticeships, young cats take the basic tools with which they were born and hone them, taking the first steps along the paths they will travel as adult cats. But in the dark of the night, as the newly promoted warrior stands watch alone, it is only natural to look back on what has been so as to take full advantage of what's to come.

Before you proceed with the next phases of developing your *Warriors Adventure Game* character, take a few seconds to look over what you've done so far. Get a firm idea in your head of where your cat is, as well as where he or she hopes to go. This will help you as you make the decisions ahead.

In this chapter you will make the first increases to your cat's Ability scores, improving on the raw gifts with which he or she was born. You will also select a handful of Knacks for your character—special tricks or maneuvers he or she learned as an apprentice.

Room to Grow

By the time you finish this chapter, your character will be ready to face any adventure in the *Warriors Adventure Game*, but that doesn't mean that he or she is *done*. One of the great things about this game is that your cat will continue to grow and learn and get better at things as you continue to play.

Advancement and growth are essential parts of life, and they are just as essential in a role-playing game. Remember that the choices you make here will create further opportunities down the road. At the end of this chapter, your character likely will not yet have reached all the heights of which he or she dreams, but that's okay. There will be plenty of opportunities for your cat to develop more. And the tools you give him or her now will determine how easy or difficult it is to achieve those larger goals later.

Ability Score Increases

In the *Warriors Adventure Game*, the changes that cats go through as they age are represented by increases to the cat's Ability scores. This happens especially quickly for apprentices.

During the course of his or her apprenticeship, your cat will have grown enough to merit two Ability increases. First, add +1 to your cat's Strength score on your character sheet. This represents the fact that he or she is now fully grown. There is certainly room to grow bigger by adding muscle, but your character is now large enough to be considered full grown.

Second, add +1 to either your cat's Intelligence or Spirit score, whichever you prefer. This represents the lessons learned during training as an apprentice. When you've chosen which Ability your cat feels is more important, add that +1 to that score on your character sheet.

Remember, this is not the end of your cat's development. As he or she grows and has more adventures, there will be regular opportunities to increase Ability scores.

Muddyclaw

Now that Muddypaw is ready to be promoted to a warrior, he's also ready to receive his warrior's name. Rather than Muddypaw, from here on we'll call him Muddyclaw.

Having grown a fair bit during his apprenticeship, Muddyclaw raises his Strength score from 1 to 2. He's still not especially large or strong, but he's definitely more impressive than he was before.

One of the things Muddyclaw learned during his training was exactly what it takes to be a medicine cat (which is his dream). He knows that things he'll have to do mostly center around Intelligence, so he decides to put his extra point into that, raising it from 2 to 3.

Finally, Muddyclaw's player marks all these changes on the character sheet, and a warrior is born.

Knacks

As cats mature, they learn tricks for dealing with different situations, trying a variety of ways of doing things and finding what works best for them. These little tricks of behavior are represented in the *Warriors Adventure Game* by Knacks. At first, Knacks might seem the same as Skills, but there are a few important differences.

Skills represent things *all* cats can do. Having points in a Skill simply means that your character does it better than others. Knacks, however, are specialized actions that must be learned *before* they can be used. In other words, if you have not written the Knack on your character sheet, then your cat cannot use that Knack.

Another difference between Knacks and Skills lies in how they are used in the game. This will be discussed later (in Chapter Five), but in brief, Skills are something your character can always use—they are *automatically* included whenever they would be appropriate. Knacks, on the other hand, are special maneuvers that your cat will have to *choose* to employ.

Finally, while Skills are free to use, Knacks each have a "cost" associated with using them. This cost, described as a number of "chips," is included in the write-ups in this chapter, but it will be fully explained in Chapter Five. As a general rule, though, the higher your cat's score in a certain Ability, the more "chips" he or she will be able to spend on Knacks related to that Ability.

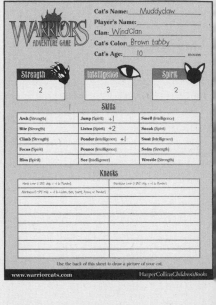

Cat's Name: Muddyclaw
Player's Name:
Clan: WindClan
Cat's Color: Brown tabby
Cat's Age: 10 moons

Strength	Intelligence	Spirit
2	3	2

Skills

Arch (Strength)	Jump (Spirit) +1	Smell (Intelligence)
Bite (Strength)	Listen (Spirit) +2	Sneak (Spirit)
Climb (Strength)	Ponder (Intelligence) +1	Swat (Intelligence)
Focus (Spirit)	Pounce (Intelligence)	Swim (Strength)
Hiss (Spirit)	See (Intelligence)	Wrestle (Strength)

Knacks

Herb Lore (1 INT chip = +1 to Ponder)	Medicine Lore (1 INT chip = +1 to Ponder)
Alertness (1 SPT chip = +1 to Listen, See, Smell, Pounce or Ponder)	

Use the back of this sheet to draw a picture of your cat.

www.warriorcats.com HarperCollins*Children'sBooks*

Muddyclaw

Since these are the things that really define a cat, Muddyclaw wants to choose Knacks that will help him in his goals and play up his best features.

The most important thing to Muddyclaw is his desire to become a medicine cat. He identifies two Knacks that will help him in that goal—Medicine Lore and Herb Lore—so he chooses them both.

With his one remaining choice, Muddyclaw picks Alertness because it is a way to even further advance the effectiveness of his Listen Skill and, at the same time, give a potential boost to several other Skills, too.

Once Muddyclaw is certain about these choices, the player writes these Knacks onto the character sheet. The player also makes brief notes about how the Knacks work, based on the write-ups, so that it will be easier to use them during the game.

Choosing Knacks

When an apprentice is promoted to a warrior, he or she has learned three Knacks. At this stage you must select three separate Knacks—you cannot choose a single Knack more than once, even if its description says that is allowed. As your character advances, you may use the extra Knack choices you get to improve any Knacks that are allowed to be chosen more than once.

Since Knacks are things that a cat must learn before he or she can use them, they are also an important way to make your character different from others. The Knacks you choose will not only define what your cat can do during play, they will define how the other characters perceive your cat.

If it is important to your cat to be thought of as smart or strong or charismatic, then you should choose Knacks that emphasize these aspects of his or her character. Once you choose a Knack, your cat has it forever—you do not need to choose it a second time. However, some Knacks provide your character with extra advantages if he or she selects it more than once. The details are described in the write-ups. These write-ups can seem a little complicated when you read them one after another, so you may want to refer to the "Knacks at a Glance" sidebar to get a general idea of what your choices are.

Just as with Skills and Ability scores, there are no "wrong" decisions to be made here. As long as you select Knacks that suit your cat's personality and goals, you will have made the "right" choice.

Skills vs. Knacks

The differences between Skills and Knacks can be a little tricky to understand at first. They will be explained fully in Chapter Five, but for now let's look at a basic example. Muddyclaw has training in the Listen Skill, and he also has chosen the Alertness Knack. Here's how they work.

Every time Muddyclaw is asked to make a Listen Check, he adds together his Intelligence score (because Listen is an Intelligence-based Skill) and the bonus he gets from his Listen Skill. Right now that's a total of 5 (3 from Intelligence, 2 from Listen). No matter what, that is the least he can get on a Listen Check.

Of course, Muddyclaw can add to that total by spending Intelligence chips (because Listen is an Intelligence-based Skill). For every Intelligence chip he spends, he increases the Check by +1.

In addition, because he has chosen the Alertness Knack, Muddyclaw can also spend a Spirit chip to activate that Knack, which will add +1 to the Check. (Spending chips will be fully explained in Chapter Five.) And, based on the description of the Alertness Knack, he can do this as many times as he has additional Spirit chips to pay for it. If he doesn't spend any Spirit chips, then Alertness doesn't affect the Check.

So, for the sake of fun, let's figure out just how high a Listen Check Muddyclaw can generate if he puts all his effort into it. First of all, he gets 3 from his Intelligence score plus 2 from his Listen Skill. Then he spends all three of his Intelligence chips, getting a +3 bonus. Then he spends both of his Spirit chips to activate the Alertness Knack twice, giving him an additional +2 bonus. So his total is 3 + 2 + 3 + 2 = 10.

The best result Muddyclaw can get on a Listen Check is 10, which is a really big number. He should be able to hear just about anything with that sort of result. Of course, he'd also be out of both Intelligence and Spirit chips, but that's a different problem.

Knacks at a Glance

Knacks, by their nature, are a little complicated. Each one is a trick that lets a character "break the rules" of the game in a small way and gain some kind of short-term advantage. So reading them can be a bit confusing, especially the first time through. The list below should help you get a better handle on what the Knacks are and what they do, and make it easier for you to decide which Knacks might be best for your cat. After scanning these, though, be sure to read the full entries to see exactly how the Knacks you're interested in work.

Alertness: Allows your cat to be more attentive to things going on near him or her.

Animal Lore: Your cat has a great deal of knowledge about other animals (but not Twolegs).

Balance: Helps your cat to move safely along branches, fences, and other precarious places.

Belly Rake: A fighting maneuver used when Wrestling, it does extra damage to your opponent.

Chomp: Powerful Bite attack that temporarily immobilizes your victim.

Clan Lore: Your cat has a great deal of knowledge about the Clans and cats in general.

Dash: Your cat can run faster and farther than usual.

Dodge: An improvement on the Jump Skill, useful to avoid damage in fights.

Feint: Use misdirection and quick movements to improve accuracy with Swat attacks.

Herb Lore: Your cat has a great deal of knowledge about healing herbs and how to treat illnesses.

Hide: Your cat is particularly clever at finding spots to sit still and hide.

Interpret Dreams: The ability to get accurate meaning out of dreams and prophecies.

Launch: A fighting maneuver used when Wrestling, it flings your opponent away.

Leap: Your cat can Pounce over a farther distance than normal.

Medicine Lore: Your cat has a great deal of knowledge about illness and injuries.

Mighty Swat: A fighting maneuver that lets your cat do extra damage with Swat attacks.

Orate: Your cat is good at giving speeches and motivating others.

Pathfinder: Your cat has a very good sense of direction and almost never gets lost.

Pin: A fighting maneuver used when Wrestling, it immobilizes your opponent.

Pummel: A fighting maneuver that relies on brute force.

Spring: Your cat can do a special kind of Pounce that goes very high straight up in the air.

Stalk: Your cat is particularly clever when it comes to sneaking up on others.

Track: Your cat is particularly good at following someone using his or her sight, hearing, and sense of smell.

Twoleg Lore: Your cat has a great deal of knowledge about Twolegs, their nests, and their beasts.

Yowl: Your cat can shout out messages over long distances.

Alertness

(1 Spirit chip)—Alertness allows your cat to be even more attentive than usual to things that are happening in the general area.

By spending 1 Spirit chip, you may use Alertness to add 1 bonus point to a single Check involving one of the following Skill Checks: Focus, Listen, Ponder, See, or Smell.

You may use Alertness more than once on a single Check, provided you pay for each use separately.

You may choose the Alertness Knack a second time. If you do, you now gain 2 bonus points whenever you use Alertness instead of just 1. You may not choose Alertness more than twice.

Animal Lore

(1 Intelligence chip)—Having the Animal Lore Knack means that your cat has a great deal of knowledge about animals (not including Twolegs).

By spending 1 Intelligence chip, you may add 1 bonus point to a single Intelligence or Ponder Check involving knowledge about or predicting the behavior of an animal.

You may choose Animal Lore more than once. For each additional time you choose this Knack, the bonus you receive for using it goes up by +1. So if you choose Animal Lore twice you get 2 bonus points each time, if you choose it three times you get 3 bonus points, etc.

Balance

(1 Spirit chip)—The Balance Knack helps a cat to move safely along branches, fence tops, and other precarious spaces.

By spending 1 Spirit chip, you may add 1 bonus point to a Climb or Strength Check made to keep from falling off a perch or ledge.

You may use Balance more than once on a single Check, provided you pay for each use separately.

Belly Rake

(2 Strength chips)—Belly Rake is a Knack your cat may use in a fight. It involves striking with your cat's back claws to injure an opponent's underbelly.

In order to use Belly Rake, your cat and the opponent must already be Wrestling. (You cannot use Belly Rake, however, if your opponent is currently successfully using the Pin Knack on you—see the Pin Knack for details.) If you are Wrestling, by spending 2 Strength chips your cat lashes out with his or her rear paws into the opponent's belly with claws extended. This is treated like a Swat attack but does 1 extra point of damage to the opponent.

You may choose the Belly Rake Knack a second time. If you do, reduce the cost of using it to 1 Strength chip rather than 2.

Chomp

(3 Strength chips)—A Chomp is a vicious type of Bite attack. Using it temporarily disables the target and lets your cat do extra damage.

You must announce that you plan to use Chomp and spend the Strength chips for it *before* you resolve the Bite attack (so if your Bite fails, you will have spent the Strength chips already). If you succeed in using a Chomp, your Bite does damage normally but you also have two additional effects.

First, your opponent is immobilized as though you have him or her Pinned (as detailed in the Pin Knack). This effect lasts until the start of your next turn.

Second, at the start of your next turn you have the choice of either holding on or letting go. If you hold on, your opponent remains Pinned until your next turn. If you let go, you do damage to your opponent as though you had landed a second successful Bite attack.

Clan Lore

(1 Intelligence chip)—Having the Clan Lore Knack means that your cat has a great deal of knowledge about the history of the Clans and cats in general.

By spending 1 Intelligence chip, you may add 1 bonus point to a single Intelligence or Ponder Check involving knowledge of the history, habits, or beliefs of Clans and Clan cat culture.

You may choose Clan Lore more than once. For each additional time you choose this Knack, the bonus you receive for using it goes up by +1. So if you choose Clan Lore twice you get 2 bonus points each time, if you choose it three times you get 3 bonus points, etc.

Dash

(1 Strength chip)—Using the Dash Knack lets your cat move very quickly, dodging obstacles and springing off nearby objects to cover more ground than running normally allows.

By spending 1 Strength chip, you may move up to twice as far as you normally would in one turn. Some obstacles prevent the use of Dash (examples include thick mud, objects that must be Climbed, and other items that cannot be easily leaped or avoided). If these kinds of obstacles are present, the Narrator should tell you so *before* you spend the Strength chip.

Dodge

(1 Spirit chip)—The Dodge Knack is an improvement on the Jump Skill. It represents a cat being able to Leap more quickly and surely out of harm's way.

You may use the Dodge Knack any time your cat makes a Jump Check simply by spending the 1 Spirit chip cost. Doing so adds 1 bonus point to the Jump Check.

You may choose the Dodge Knack up to a maximum of three times. Each time you choose this Knack, the bonus you receive for using it goes up by +1. So if you choose Dodge twice you get 2 bonus points each time, and 3 bonus points if you choose it three times. You may not choose Dodge more than three times.

Feint

(1 Intelligence chip)—Using the Feint Knack, your cat can use misdirection and quick movement to improve the accuracy of his or her Swat attacks.

By spending 1 Intelligence chip, you may add 1 bonus point to a Swat attack, making it more likely to hit but *not* adding any additional damage.

You may choose the Feint Knack up to three times. For each time that you choose it, increase the bonus this Knack grants by +1. So if you choose Feint twice, you get 2 bonus points every time you use it, if you choose it a third time the bonus becomes +3. You may not choose Feint more than three times.

Herb Lore

(1 Intelligence chip)—Having the Herb Lore Knack means that your cat has a great deal of knowledge about healing herbs and other natural remedies. You know how to treat various injuries and illnesses, even if you can't diagnose them.

By spending 1 Intelligence chip, you may add 1 bonus point to a single Intelligence or Ponder Check involving knowledge or use of herbs and other healing substances.

You may choose Herb Lore more than once. For each additional time you choose this Knack, the bonus you receive for using it goes up by +1. So if you choose Herb Lore twice you get 2 bonus points each time, if you choose it three times you get 3 bonus points, etc.

Hide

(1 Spirit chip)—The Hide Knack represents a cat being particularly clever at finding spots in which he or she is difficult to see.

By spending 1 Spirit chip, you may add 2 bonus points to a Sneak Check if your cat is sitting still in a single spot and not moving. As soon as the cat moves, this bonus is lost entirely.

You may use Hide more than once on a single Sneak Check, provided you pay for each use separately.

Interpret Dreams

(2 Spirit chips)—The Interpret Dreams Knack indicates that a cat has the ability to find accurate meaning in dreams or prophecies sent by StarClan.

By spending 2 Spirit chips, your character can find some measure of sense in messages from StarClan or in prophecies of old (that is, if the time is right and if there is any sense to be found in them). These insights may not make everything crystal clear, but they should at least give some clues as to what StarClan expects the cats to do or where further answers can be found. This Knack may also tell you that a dream is just an ordinary one or that a prophecy does *not* have any immediate application.

You may choose the Interpret Dreams Knack a second time. If you do, reduce the cost of using it to 1 Spirit chip rather than 2. You may not choose Interpret Dreams more than twice.

Launch

(3 Strength chips)—The Launch Knack represents a combat maneuver that allows a cat to fling an opponent away, providing a momentary respite.

In order to use the Launch Knack, your cat and the opponent must already be Wrestling. (It is one of the few offensive maneuvers that a cat *can* perform while being Pinned.) If the combatants are Wrestling, by spending 3 Strength chips your cat may thrust out with the back paws in an attempt to hurl the opponent away through the air. If you win the Wrestling Check, the opponent will land two body lengths away and be disoriented enough that he or she cannot perform any kind of attack on his or her next action.

You may use Launch up to four times on a single Wrestling Check, provided you pay for each use separately. Each additional use of Launch increases the distance your opponent flies by one body length. So if your cat chooses this Knack twice, using it hurls the opponent three body lengths away. Choosing it three times allows your cat to hurl an opponent four body lengths away, and so on. You may not use Launch more than four times on a single Wrestling Check.

You may choose the Launch Knack a second time. If you do, reduce the cost of using it to 2 Spirit chips rather than 3. You may not choose Launch more than twice.

Leap

(1 Strength chip)—The Leap Knack represents a special kind of Pounce in which the cat tries to cover more distance without worrying about being able to land cleanly.

By spending 1 Strength chip, your cat may increase the distance covered by a Pounce by up to one body length. However, the price of doing this is an uncontrolled landing. Depending on the situation, the Narrator may rule that your cat suffers damage or faces some other appropriate difficulty.

You may use Leap up to four times on a single Pounce Check, provided you pay for each use separately. Since the maximum number of times you may use Leap on a single Pounce Check is four, the maximum extra distance you may cover is four extra body lengths.

Medicine Lore

(1 Intelligence chip)—Having the Medicine Lore Knack means that your cat has a great deal of knowledge about injuries and illnesses. You can recognize what is ailing a sick or hurt cat, even if you don't know how to treat the problem.

By spending 1 Intelligence chip, you may add 1 bonus point to a single Intelligence or Ponder Check involving diagnosing what is wrong with a sick or injured cat.

You may choose Medicine Lore more than once. For each additional time you choose this knack, the bonus you receive for using it goes up by +1. So if you choose Medicine Lore twice you get 2 bonus points each time, if you choose it three times you get 3 bonus points, etc.

Mighty Swat

(2 Strength chips)— Mighty Swat is a Knack your cat might use in a fight. It allows you to cause more damage with your Swat attack.

By spending 2 Strength chips, you may do 1 extra point of damage with your Swat attack. However, you must declare that you are using Mighty Swat at the start of the attack, so the Strength chips must be spent whether the blow hits or not.

You may use Mighty Swat more than once on a single Swat, provided you pay for each use separately (and before the attack is resolved).

You may choose the Mighty Swat Knack a second time. If you do, reduce the cost of using it to 1 Strength chip rather than 2. You may not choose Mighty Swat more than twice.

Orate

(1 Spirit chip)—The Orate Knack represents being a cat who is a skilled speaker, capable of motivating and inspiring those who are listening.

By spending 1 Spirit chip, you may add 1 bonus point to any Spirit, Focus, or Ponder Check made to figure out what fellow cats are thinking, to make a plan that others will find appealing, or to make a speech that will inspire friends and allies to take a particular course of action.

You may choose Orate more than once. For each additional time you choose this Knack, the bonus you receive for using it goes up by +1. So if you choose Orate twice you get 2 bonus points each time, if you choose it three times you get 3 bonus points, etc.

It is important to note, though, that Orate does not work on other players' cats. It is up to you, as a player, to motivate them. Orate only works on cats who are controlled by the Narrator.

Pathfinder

(1 Intelligence chip)—The Pathfinder Knack represents being a cat with a keen sense of direction. It allows you to be aware of where you are in relation to other known sites—how far from your Clan's camp you are, what direction a certain hollow tree is, etc.

By spending 1 Intelligence chip, you can get an accurate feeling for one of the following: the distance to a known place, the direction to a known place, what places that you know are near your current location.

You may choose the Pathfinder Knack a second time. If you do, you can get two of the listed pieces of information each time you use Pathfinder. You may not choose Pathfinder more than twice.

Pin

(3 Strength chips)—Pin is a Knack your cat might use in a fight, specifically when Wrestling. It allows one cat to immobilize his or her opponent.

In order to use Pin, your cat and the opponent must already be Wrestling. By spending 3 Strength chips, you can use the weight of your cat's body to force the opponent to the ground, where he or she cannot move. The Pin lasts until the opponent wins a Wrestling Check or the cat who started the Pin gets up or is forced off the opponent.

While Pinned, the only physical actions a cat may take are: start a Wrestling Check to try to escape, use the Launch Knack to try to escape, Swat at the Pinning cat, Bite the Pinning cat (but remember that Biting other cats is strictly forbidden by the warrior code).

You may choose the Pin Knack a second time. If you do, reduce the cost of using it to 2 Strength chips rather than 3. You may not choose Pin more than twice.

Pummel

(3 Strength chips)—Pummel is a Knack your cat might use in a fight. It allows you to make a Swat attack that relies on brute force to hit rather than strategic placement of the blow.

By spending 3 Strength chips, you can make the equivalent of a Swat attack based on a Strength Check rather than an Intelligence Check. It is the equivalent of your cat attempting to overpower his or her opponent rather than land accurate blows. Damage is determined normally.

You may choose the Pummel Knack a second time. If you do, reduce the cost of using it to 2 Strength chips rather than 3. You may not choose Pummel more than twice.

Spring

(3 Strength chips)—The Spring Knack represents a special kind of Pounce in which the cat tries to stretch his or her paws as high as possible, often to bat at an object.

By spending 3 Strength chip, your cat may Spring at an object that normally would be too high to reach. The maximum height that a cat can Spring is twice the height that he or she can normally Pounce.

You may choose the Spring Knack up to three times. The second time you choose it, reduce the cost of using Spring to 2 Strength chips rather than 3. The third time you choose it, reduce the cost to 1 Strength chip. You may not choose Spring more than three times.

Stalk

(1 Spirit chip)—The Stalk Knack represents a cat being particularly clever at remaining undetected while he or she is moving.

By spending 1 Spirit chip, you may add 2 bonus points to a Sneak Check if your cat is trying to approach a target unawares. While the cat can pause momentarily to avoid detection, if he or she comes to a complete and extended halt, this bonus is lost even if movement begins again.

You may use Stalk more than once on a single Sneak Check, provided you pay for each use separately.

Track

(1 Intelligence chip)—Track is a Knack that cats use to trace the movements of an animal or another cat. It can be of great use when hunting prey or trying to find what path another cat took when traveling nearby.

By spending 1 Intelligence chip, you may use Track to add 1 bonus point to a single attempt to follow the movements of a living creature by using one of the following Skill Checks: Listen, See, or Smell.

You may use Track more than once on a single Check, provided you pay for each use separately.

You may choose the Track Knack a second time. If you do, you gain 2 bonus points whenever you use Track instead of just 1. You may not choose Track more than twice.

Twoleg Lore

(1 Intelligence chip)—Having the Twoleg Lore Knack means that your cat has a great deal of knowledge about the behavior of Twolegs and the dangers posed by them and their monsters.

By spending 1 Intelligence chip, you may add 1 bonus point to a single Intelligence or Ponder Check involving Twolegs, their nests, and their monsters.

You may choose Twoleg Lore more than once. For each additional time you choose this Knack, the bonus you receive for using it goes up by +1. So if you choose Twoleg Lore twice you get 2 bonus points each time, if you choose it three times you get 3 bonus points, etc.

Yowl

(1 Intelligence chip)—The Yowl Knack represents a cat using growls and other vocal warnings to inform others nearby that he or she is particularly upset.

By spending 1 Intelligence chip, you may add 1 bonus point to an Arch or a Hiss Check.

Alternatively, your cat can use Yowl to yell out to any other cat within hearing range. This Yowl can carry one very basic message such as "Danger," "Help me," "Enemies are here," or something similar.

You may choose the Yowl Knack up to three times. Each time you choose it, the bonus it grants increases by +1 and the distance from which a message can be heard increases. The maximum bonus is 3 points, and the maximum distance a Yowl can be heard is as far as a cat can travel in an hour.

Ready to Play

At this point, your character is a fully trained warrior capable of taking his or her place in Clan life. That does not mean that your character is "done," though.

All living things continue to learn and grow as they go along, and your cat is no exception. As you play the *Warriors Adventure Game*, your cat will master new Skills, learn new Knacks, and continue to see changes in his or her Ability scores. The methods by which these changes take place are discussed in Chapter Four.

However, if you are anxious to get right into the adventure, skip ahead to Chapter Five. There you will find the details you'll need to take information you've just put on your character sheet and use it in the game.

Chapter Four: Life Lessons

Your character sheet is filled out and your cat is ready —now you can start playing the *Warriors Adventure Game*. As time passes, though, your cat will continue growing and learning, and this will mean adding to and changing the information written on your character sheet. From time to time, you'll probably want to copy the information onto a *new* character sheet, just to keep things clean and clear.

The first thing you'll want to be certain of is that the information on your character sheet actually matches the ideas you have of your cat in your mind. If it doesn't, you should make adjustments to bring everything in line. You've done a lot of work so far, and it wouldn't be right for you to have less fun because you made one or two small mistakes early on.

Once you're sure that you have the character you want, though, you'll still be given the opportunity occasionally to improve your cat's abilities or add new ones to his or her character sheet. This is sometimes called "leveling up," and it is one of the best parts of any role-playing adventure game.

Changing Your Cat

As you play through one or two adventures, you'll learn more about the *Warriors Adventure Game*. You'll get to understand how the rules work in greater detail. In addition, the more you play, the better you'll understand your character.

As you play the game, you may realize that you regret a few of the choices you made while filling out your cat's character sheet. You might have misunderstood which Skills would apply to certain situations, or thought that a Knack would be more useful than it turned out to be in practice. Whatever the details, there is no reason you should be forced to play the game with an incorrect version of your cat.

Making Minor Adjustments

If the mistakes are relatively small—an adjustment to how you distributed your cat's Ability scores, or swapping one Skill or Knack for another—you can just make those changes. Be certain to tell the other players, though.

In fact, after you play through your first adventure (especially if it is "Saving the Kits," found in Chapter Eight), it might be a good idea for all the players to talk a little bit about the game and the experience of playing it. Together, you may be able to help one another make small adjustments to all your cats so that everyone is happier with his or her results and future adventures are more enjoyable.

However, it's possible that the frustrations are deeper and will require more than a few minor adjustments to fix. You may have to make more major adjustments or even start a new character from scratch.

Starting from Scratch

It may just be that you don't enjoy playing the cat character you have created. Maybe what seemed like a good idea at the start of this process turned out to be less fun or more difficult than you first thought. Or maybe you realized that it would be more fun to play a different kind of cat.

That's okay.

If you're truly unhappy with your cat, you can always put aside the character sheet you've been working on, print out a clean one, and start over from the beginning. Bear in mind the lessons that you learned and the mistakes you made and create a character that's more to your liking.

Remember, though, that some things that seem like imperfections may just be due to the fact that at this stage your character is still rather young. If the vision in your head is of a fully mature cat and one of the Clan's most important members, then the problem probably isn't one of character design—it's one of time. Your cat needs time to grow into the character you want him or her to be.

If everyone in the group would rather play more mature cats, that's a different problem. Rather than starting from scratch, you'll instead have to make more major adjustments to the cats you already have.

Making Major Adjustments

If you are not going to simply start from scratch and create a whole new cat, major adjustments to your character will almost certainly entail making him or her older and, thus, more experienced. It is best that you wait until you've played a few adventures using the *Warriors Adventure Game* before you attempt this.

Making these sorts of changes will require you to pick a greater number of Skills and Knacks and make repeated adjustments to your Ability scores, and it can be a fairly involved process. Any mistakes you make along the way will add up over time, making them more difficult to find and fix later.

When you finish the character creation process described in Chapters Two and Three, your newly promoted warrior will be about 10 moons old. Remember that life is harder for Clan cats than it is for kittypets. A warrior's life is much more intense, and that generally means it's harder and often much shorter.

A seasoned warrior who has had time to become a mainstay of the Clan will usually be about 20 moons old. A senior warrior, looked up to as a mainstay of the Clan and a cat who might be considered for an important role such as deputy, will usually be about 30 moons old. By the time a cat reaches 50 moons old, he or she will begin to slow down—although still sharp of mind, the cat's body will begin to show signs of age. After 70 moons old, a cat will usually cease being an active warrior and will take up the mantle of being an elder in the Clan.

Confused? Don't worry. This is a lot of information to try to digest all at once. If you want to get a better handle on it, look at the "Changes Over Time" chart in the "Improving Your Cat" section. Once you've decided how old you want your characters to be, it's a fairly straightforward (though time-consuming) process to use the information in that section to advance your cat's character sheet to the proper stage.

Getting Older

Your cat's character sheet will be very different at different times in his or her life. As stated in the "Making Major Adjustments" section, at the end of the character creation process it is assumed that your cat is 10 moons old. From that point on, how do you know for sure what age your cat is?

In the Warriors novels, time doesn't always pass at the same rate. Sometimes as much as a whole moon passes between the end of one chapter and the beginning of the next. The speed of time passing changes depending on the needs of the story. Likewise, the passage of time can happen in several ways for your characters. The choice, in many cases, is up to you.

Age by Real Time

One of the easiest ways is to have your cat age according to real time. That is, for every day that passes for you, one passes for your cat. This may be easy, but it's probably not going to be very exciting; since the effects of aging only happen on a monthly basis, it will take a long time for you to see much change at all.

A similar idea is to use an adaptation of real time. For instance, for every week that passes for you,

one moon passes for your cat. This is more likely to be satisfying for you, let your characters grow noticeably, and keep the game changing in interesting ways.

Age by Adventure

Some of the adventures for the *Warriors Adventure Game* will say specifically that a certain amount of time passes. This might happen at the beginning or end of the adventure or, on rare occasions, even in the middle. When it does, it's an automatic chance for your cat to get better in one or more areas.

Age by Choice

Finally, as a group, the players may want to decide on a completely personal schedule for aging. There are several ways to do this. For instance, the group might decide that at the end of every adventure the cats get a bit older (anywhere from 1 to 6 moons).

Alternatively, rather than making a regular and scheduled thing, the group could ignore aging for a while. They could go through an adventure or two without any changes to the characters, then have the cats age a significant amount all at once. (This should probably be no fewer than 6 moons at a time so that the effects are significant enough for everyone to notice.)

Improving Your Cat

There are several ways your character will improve over time. Some of them will happen automatically as your cat gets older, while others will be tied to playing through and completing adventures. But they all fall into three types of improvements: Knacks, Skills, and Ability scores.

Knacks

As we discussed in Chapter Three, your cat has to learn a particular Knack before he or she can use it. Every chance you get to choose new Knacks for your character is a chance to make your cat different from the others and bring him or her closer to being as you imagined.

At the end of every adventure they complete, each cat will learn at least one new Knack. Also, many of the adventures for the *Warriors Adventure Game* will specify points in the middle, generally between chapters, when the characters can gain specific new Knacks—things they had the opportunity to learn during the previous scenes.

Even if they aren't having adventures, your cats will naturally learn Knacks as they get older. Cats learn a new Knack or get the chance to improve an existing one once every few moons. You can see these as well as other changes your cat will undergo in the "Changes Over Time" chart.

Skills

Your cat's Skills improve more slowly than his or her Knacks; but, by their nature, when they do, it will have a bigger impact on game play (since Skills work automatically but you have to choose to use a Knack).

Some adventures in the *Warriors Adventure Game* will offer opportunities for characters to gain or improve specific Skills. Generally, this will happen after a scene that features the use of those Skills or at the end of the adventure.

In addition to those gained through adventures, cats naturally learn Skills over time, just as they do Knacks —only slightly less quickly. You can see these as well as other changes your cat will undergo in the "Changes Over Time" chart.

Age in Moons	Effect from Growth
11	Skill
12	+1 Any Ability
13	Knack
14	+1 Intelligence or Spirit
15	Skill
16	Knack
17	+1 Any Ability
19	Skill and Knack
21	+1 Any Ability
22	Knack
23	Skill
25	Knack
26	+1 Intelligence or Spirit
27	Skill
28	Knack
31	Skill and Knack
32	+1 Any Ability
34	Knack
35	Skill
37	Knack
38	+1 Intelligence
39	Skill
40	Knack
43	Knack and Skill
45	+1 Any Ability
46	Knack
47	Skill
49	Knack
50	+1 Spirit
51	Skill
52	Knack
55	Knack and Skill
57	–1 Strength
58	Knack
59	Skill
61	Knack
62	+1 Any Ability
63	Skill
64	Knack
67	Knack and Skill
68	–1 Strength
69	+1 Spirit
70	Knack

Ability Scores

The least predictable of the changes a cat goes through are those to his or her Ability scores. They aren't learned actions that your character can practice—they are a natural part of growth and maturation. Improvements happen more frequently in a cat's youth, occur less frequently in the middle of life, and begin to reverse themselves with Ability score losses as old age approaches. The only certainty is that your character's Ability scores will be in flux throughout his or her entire life.

The pattern for Ability score changes is less regular than those for Skills or Knacks. To make tracking this information easier, the "Changes Over Time" chart lists when you should raise or lower an Ability score, as well as when you can improve or choose new Knacks and Skills.

Changes Over Time

As time passes, your cat will continue to change in a variety of ways. The following table tracks these changes moon by moon. Every time another new moon passes, check to see if your cat has matured in any way in the "Changes Over Time" chart.

Chapter Five: Playing the Game

You've created a cat character of your own, advanced him or her up from an apprentice into a newly promoted warrior, and now you're ready to play. But as you've no doubt realized by now, the *Warriors Adventure Game* is different from most games you've played before.

Just looking at your character sheet, it's easy to get a little intimidated by all the terms and numbers. So before you move on to your first adventure, let's go over what you need to play the game and what to expect from the experience.

What You Need

In order to play the *Warriors Adventure Game*, you'll need a few basic supplies. Chief among these is a group of friends to play with.

The game is best played in a small group of 3–6. You can certainly proceed with only 2 people and there is no maximum number; but once your group gets so big you can't all sit together and talk comfortably, it will become more and more difficult to enjoy the game. Different groups will find that they prefer different numbers of players, and the only way to find out what works best for you and your friends is to try a few different arrangements.

The *Warriors Adventure Game* is a storytelling game, so it is important that you have a comfortable place to sit while you play—preferably a place where you can sit around in a loose circle or at a comfortable table. Also, since all the players will be doing a fair bit of talking, it would be a good idea if everyone had a drink of some sort.

Once you're all gathered and comfortable, there are still a few basic items that you'll find helpful during the game.

Character Sheets

It is important that every player have a completed and legible listing of all the details about his or her character. You'll be referencing it a lot during the game.

Ability Chips

Each player will also need three different types of chips (small stones, coins, pips, beads, or other markers) and a pouch or bag in which to hold them.

The reason three different kinds of chips are required is that they represent the Strength, Intelligence, and Spirit chips that your character has to spend during the course of the game. Everyone in the group can use the same chips, or each player can bring his or her own. All that matters is that you can easily and quickly tell the difference between them while you're playing.

Each player gets a number of chips equal to his or her character's score in the appropriate Ability. So a player whose cat has Ability scores of Strength 3, Intelligence 2, Spirit 1 would get three Strength chips, two Intelligence chips, and one Spirit chip.

If there aren't enough actual chips to go around, players may use a piece of scrap paper to keep track of their available Strength, Intelligence, and Spirit chips. But since the number of chips you have will change frequently throughout the game, tracking the values this way must be done very carefully.

Paper and Pencil

Since this is a storytelling game, you may want to make notes about important facts you learn during the course of play—the names of cats you meet or locations you can go, the details of what a cat tells you, etc. You may also want to pass notes between each other so that you don't interrupt someone else while he or she is speaking. There may also be times when you want to keep certain thoughts secret from the Narrator or other players based on what is going on in the story.

Paper can also come in handy for the Narrator to sketch out a rough map that shows where the cats are in relation to some important character or object.

An Adventure

Finally, you'll need an adventure to play. There is a mini-adventure in Chapter Eight, which should be enough to get you started and let you become familiar with how the game is played.

One of the good things about the *Warriors Adventure Game* is that there are different paths through every story, and you will almost certainly not exhaust them all your first time through. You can always play through an adventure more than once and see how the outcome changes if you make different decisions along the way.

In addition, there are full-length adventures in the back of each novel in the Warriors: Omen of the Stars series. And you can always check www.warriorcats.com for more information.

How to Do Everything

A good deal of the *Warriors Adventure Game* will consist of you and your friends talking about the situations described in the adventures and how your characters want to react to them.

Most of the time, your cats will be able to do what you describe—there isn't a lot of fun in making rules for every little thing that a cat does during the day. However, when the result of an action is uncertain and dramatically important to the story, you will use the information on your character sheet to decide the outcome.

This is not just a matter of looking up numbers on your character sheet. You will use your Abilities, Skills, and Knacks in different kinds of Checks.

Ability Checks

The most common kind of action in the game is an Ability Check. This is a test of a basic Ability, such as if your cat is strong enough to push a fallen branch out of the way or smart enough to figure out where a lost kit might have wandered.

The difficulty of the Ability Check will be written in the adventure. If your cat's Ability score is equal to or higher than the difficulty for the Check, you succeed. If it is lower, you fail. (The adventure will tell the Narrator exactly what happens if an Ability Check succeeds or fails.) So, for example, if Muddyclaw is in the middle of an adventure that calls for a Strength Check, his player would look at the character sheet and see that Muddyclaw has a 2 in Strength. If the difficulty of this Strength Check is 2 or less, Muddyclaw succeeds. If it's 3 or higher, he fails.

Spending Ability Chips

You can give a temporary boost to your Ability score, allowing your cat to succeed at actions that at first may seem too difficult, by spending Ability chips. When you spend an Ability chip, take a chip from your pool and set it aside. For each chip you spend, you get a +1 bonus added to this particular Check. The only catch is that you must spend Ability chips that match the Check being performed. In other words, you must spend Strength chips on a Strength Check, Intelligence chips on an Intelligence Check, and Spirit chips on a Spirit Check. Unless the adventure says otherwise, you can spend as many chips as you like on a single Check. (See the "Converting Ability Chips" sidebar for an advanced rule that gives you extra options.)

Once you have spent a chip and set it aside, you cannot use it again until the Narrator tells you it's time to

refresh your Ability chips (this will happen at several points during every adventure). At that time, all the chips you've set aside come back into play and you can spend them again. So you must be careful when and on what you spend your Ability chips. Once you run out of a particular kind of chip, you cannot spend chips on that type of Check again until the Narrator tells you to refresh your Ability chips.

In the example above, Muddyclaw would have two Strength chips in his pool (because his Strength score is 2). If the player didn't think that the total provided by just Muddyclaw's Strength score was high enough for that Check, he or she could spend one of those chips to give Muddyclaw a +1 bonus on this Check, increasing his total to 3. The spent chip would be set aside, and now the player would only have one Strength chip left until the Narrator says it's time to refresh the chips.

Converting Ability Chips

The rules say that you must spend Ability chips that match the Check your cat is attempting. When you run out of a particular type, you can no longer spend chips on that kind of Ability Check. However, if you really need to, you can use this advanced rule to convert chips from one type into another.

The cost for doing so is 2 to 1.

That means you can convert 2 of the wrong type of Ability chips into 1 of the right kind. So if you needed an Intelligence chip but you only had Strength and Spirit chips left, you could trade 2 chips (1 of each or 2 of a single kind) and convert them into 1 Intelligence chip.

This can be very helpful, especially to starting warriors—who will only have 7 chips total when they play their first adventure (and apprentices have only 5 chips). As your cat gets older, the possibilities will get even greater since every time his or her Ability scores go up, so will the number of chips you have to use.

Skill Checks

Skill Checks are essentially the same as Ability Checks, except that your cat automatically gets a bonus equal to his or her level in that Skill. Remember that Skills can be ranked anywhere from 0 to 5, so any check based on a

Skill that you have not chosen during character creation or during advancement will have a total equal to the base Ability score only.

For example, if the adventure requires Muddyclaw to make a Ponder Check, his player would begin by taking the Intelligence score from the character sheet (since Ponder is a Skill based on Intelligence) then adding the level listed next to the Ponder Skill. In this case, Muddyclaw would have a 3 from Intelligence and a 1 from Ponder for a total of 4. If 4 is equal to or higher than the difficulty listed in the adventure, Muddyclaw succeeds at the Ponder Check.

But what if, instead, the adventure had called for a Focus Check? Focus is linked to Spirit, so the player would have to check Muddyclaw's Spirit score and his training in the Focus Skill. That would have been a 2 from Spirit and a 0 from Focus (since Muddyclaw isn't trained in that Skill at all, his level is 0) for a total of 2.

As with Ability Checks, you can get a bonus to a Skill Check by spending Ability chips that match the Ability linked to the Skill being used.

Using Knacks

Knacks work differently than Skills and Abilities. Your cat will never be asked to make a "Knack Check." Instead, Knacks are special abilities that are triggered only when you spend Ability chips. Some Knacks give bonus points to specific kinds of Checks. Other Knacks allow your cat to do things that he or she otherwise couldn't do.

Knacks are never automatically added into a Check. You must pay the Knack's cost with the appropriate Ability chips each time your cat wants to use it. If you do not have enough of the required Ability chips to pay for a Knack, you cannot use the Knack at that time.

In addition, you should generally tell the Narrator before you use a Knack. He or she can let you know if the situation is appropriate to do so *before* you spend Ability chips in the effort. Also, the details of an adventure may list special effects, bonuses, or (sometimes) even penalties for using certain Knacks at certain times.

Complicated Actions

All Checks follow the methods described above. However, not all actions can be resolved by a single Check. Sometimes accomplishing a complicated goal will require a series of Checks before it can be completed. Examples of complicated actions include hunting and fighting as well as things like following an old scent trail, crossing a Thunderpath, or pushing your way through a particularly tight opening.

The adventure will list the necessary Checks, sometimes specifying the order in which they must be accomplished. If there are no specifications, then the order doesn't matter.

Sometimes all the parts of a complicated action must be performed by the same character, but often this will be something players can do as a team—with one player's cat performing the first Check, another player's cat performing the second, and so on.

Unless the adventure says differently, you do not have to perform all the Checks successfully in a row. If your cat succeeds at the first Check then fails at the second one, you don't have to go back and redo the first one.

Tooth and Claw

As mentioned above, hunting and fighting are complicated actions. And since they are so important in the lives of Clan cats, they deserve special attention here. While they may be slightly more complicated than other actions, it is important to remember that at their heart they follow all the same rules as other Ability and Skill Checks.

The reason that these activities are so different is that they both involve more than a cat simply doing his or her best at an action. Hunting and fighting both involve someone else attempting to stop or evade the cat's action. In the case of hunting, it is a prey animal that would rather not be caught and eaten. In the case of fighting, it is another cat who is trying to avoid being hit while, at the same time, probably trying to hit the attacking cat with counterstrikes.

Hunting

If hunting is important to an adventure, the details will be presented in the text. But if cats are in the middle of an adventure that takes them far away from the Clan, or if players want to have a friendly bit of competition between their cats, the Narrator may want to let them do a little bit of hunting on the side.

Hunting is complicated because there are a lot of factors that go into it. The hunting cat must find prey, then catch it, and finally kill it. Plus, different animals have different abilities of their own, so a single set of difficulty numbers will not cover all hunting situations. See the section "Prey" for more details on appropriate difficulty numbers.

In any attempt to hunt there are four stages:

Locate: The cat must first find an animal to hunt. This is done by succeeding at one of the following Checks: Listen, See, or Smell.

Approach: Once the cat has found an appropriate prey animal, he or she must get close enough to attack it. This is done by succeeding at a Sneak Check. (The Stalk Knack will be especially helpful in this action.)

Grab: When the cat is close enough to the prey, he or she must get claws on it before it gets away. This is done by succeeding at a Pounce Check.

Kill: Finally, once the cat has the prey, he or she must finish it off. This is done by succeeding at a Bite Check. (The Chomp Knack will be especially helpful in this action.)

Prey

Different prey animals present different challenges in hunting. This is something that every cat has to learn and practice during his or her apprenticeship. Hunting a rabbit is different from hunting a mouse or a vole or a sparrow. Some cats may be excellent at certain kinds of hunting but only so-so at others. The key, though, lies in a combination of the Skills of the cat and the senses of the prey.

If a cat is hunting because it is an important part of an adventure, the text will tell the Narrator how difficult each of the actions is. If, however, this is an impromptu bit of hunting, the Narrator will have to set the difficulty levels based on the information below.

Mice: Locating a mouse is relatively difficult, but approaching one is fairly easy. The difficulty in grabbing a mouse varies greatly because mice tend to panic and race away blindly, but that means that they sometimes run right into the hunter's claws. Once a mouse is caught, it's easy to kill.

Rabbits: Locating a rabbit is easy but approaching it can be very difficult—rabbits have good hearing and are nervous creatures. Grabbing a rabbit can be very difficult as they are very fast and clever. Also, they are large enough so that killing them can be challenging.

Voles: Locating a vole can be challenging or even difficult. But once spotted, they are easy to approach and grab, and very easy to kill.

Sparrows: Sparrows and other small birds are very easy to spot, particularly when they are landing. However, they are very sensitive to movement and so can be challenging to approach. The most difficult thing is grabbing them, because if you miss, they will fly away —you won't get a second chance. Still, they are fairly fragile animals, so killing a sparrow is very easy.

How Easy Is Easy?

Usually when you're playing the *Warriors Adventure Game*, the target numbers for various Checks and the repercussions of success and failure will be clearly spelled out in the adventure. However, if the characters want to do anything unexpected, such as a bit of impromptu hunting, the Narrator will have to make up such details.

But how do you figure out what number a Check has to beat? How do you turn a story idea into a numerical value?

There is no exact answer, but the solution lies in figuring out how difficult you think the action is to perform. Is it something that should be accomplished easily? Something that the average cat can do successfully about half the time? Something that only the most skilled cats will ever succeed at? Once you figure out those questions, you can use the answers to get an idea of what number is right for the target.

Of course, "easy" is something that changes based on how experienced the cats are. What's "easy" for a Clan deputy might be "almost impossible" for a newly promoted warrior. But the more you play, the more you'll get a feeling for how difficult it is for your characters to reach certain target numbers.. In the meanwhile, you can use the table below. It gives approximate numbers for different levels of difficulty. These numbers are good for use with new warriors, such as the cats you and your friends have just made.

Difficulty	Range of Target #
Very Easy	1–2
Easy	2–4
Average	4–5
Challenging	5–6
Difficult	6–8
Very Difficult	8–10
Almost Impossible	11+

Fighting

Most cats prefer to live peacefully: hunting, taking care of their Clanmates, and lying in the sun. However, conflict between the Clans happens more frequently than any cat likes, and it is important that all Clan cats learn to fight and keep those skills (and their claws) sharp.

It's fairly common for cats in the same Clan to practice sparring with one another, with their claws sheathed. This allows them to build on their strengths, try to eliminate their weaknesses, and learn different strategies that might come in handy during a real battle.

If there is a lull in the middle of an adventure, or the players just want to have their cats roughhouse for a while, the Narrator may wish to suggest that they spar. That way, everyone will be more familiar with the process if it happens to come up later. Treat sparring like any other fight, except that it doesn't do any real damage.

When fighting in the *Warriors Adventure Game*, cats take turns trying to Swat or Wrestle each other. The cat with the highest Strength score goes first. If there is a tie, the cat with the most Strength chips currently goes first. If there is still a tie, then the players should use some fair method to choose who goes first (flip a coin, do rock-paper-scissors, etc.). When that cat is done, proceed to the cat with the next highest Strength score and so on. When all of the cats in the fight (including nearby cats who want to join the fight) have had a chance to perform an action, that marks the end of one Round of fighting. If the cats still want to continue fighting, start a new Round.

Swatting

Swatting is batting at an opponent using your cat's front paws. This is the most common strategy in fighting. The attacking cat will make a Swat Check (sometimes using Knacks such as Feint, Mighty Swat, or Pummel to enhance their effectiveness). At the same time, the target should make a Jump Check to try to avoid this blow (perhaps using the Dodge Knack to enhance their Jump Skill).

If the Swat Check of the attacking cat is equal to or higher than the Jump Check of the defending cat, the attack succeeds. If the result of the Swat Check is more than double the result of the Jump Check, the attacking cat gets +2 to his or her Strength Check for determining damage. (See "Doing Damage" below.) If the Jump Check is higher than the Swat Check, then the blow missed. In either case, the attacking cat's turn is over.

Wrestling

Wrestling is when two or more cats tumble together, clawing and scratching at one another. It is more dangerous than Swatting because there are more opportunities for cats to get hurt while Wrestling.

To start Wrestling, on his or her turn a cat must first make a Pounce Check while his or her target must make a Jump Check. If the Pounce Check is equal to or greater than the Jump Check, then the two cats are Wrestling. If the Jump Check is higher, then the target managed to get out of the way. In either case, the Pouncing cat's turn is over.

When two or more cats are already Wrestling, other cats may join the fighting. To do so, on his or her turn a cat must make a Pounce Check whose total is equal to or higher than the total number of cats already involved in the Wrestling. If the total is lower than that number, the cat was unable to squeeze his or her way into the battle. Either way, the Pouncing cat's turn is over.

When a cat's turn in the Round comes up, if he or she is currently Wrestling, immediately have all the cats involved make either a Wrestling Check (if they want to continue Wrestling) or a Jump Check (if they want to escape the Wrestling). Whatever cat gets the highest result for his or her Check has the momentary advantage. If that cat made a Jump Check, he or she escapes the Wrestling and can do something else on his or her turn the next Round. If that cat made a Wrestling Check, then he or she can do damage to any one opponent currently involved in the Wrestling (see "Doing Damage" below). If two or more of the Checks are tied for highest result, no one has the advantage and the Wrestling continues.

As long as there are at least two cats involved, the Wrestling will continue from Round to Round.

Doing Damage

When one cat successfully hits another in a fight, the attacking cat makes a Strength Check. Compare the total of that Check to the opponent's Strength score. In other words, the attacker can spend Ability chips to increase his or her total, but the defender cannot. Also, the effects of the Mighty Swat and Belly Rake Knacks, if applicable, are added into the attacker's total.

If the attacker's total is less than or equal to the defender's Strength score, the defending cat loses 1 chip (defender's choice) from his or her current Ability chip pool. If the attacker's total is more than the defender's Strength score, the defending cat loses 2 chips (defender's choice). If the attacker's total was more than double the defender's Strength score, the defending cat loses 3 chips (defender's choice).

Chips lost in this manner are not regained when the Narrator tells you to refresh your chips the way chips that are spent on Knacks or Checks are. Instead, take any chips lost because of damage and set them aside in their storage pouch. These represent wounds the cat has taken and *do not* come back when it is time to refresh the Ability points. The only way to get these chips back is through healing of some sort.

Biting: Biting is much more serious and does more damage. It is considered dishonorable to Bite another cat in normal combat. Although the Clans fight, these are fights for dominance or supremacy and almost never to purposely try to kill one another. Biting is only acceptable if a fight is a life-or-death struggle.

Any time damage is caused by Biting, the victim loses 1 additional chip on top of the effects described above.

Knocked Out

If a cat has no Ability chips left, then he or she is Knocked Out. This is another reason to be careful about when and how often your cat spends chips.

A Knocked Out cat cannot do anything at all until he or she has at least one chip in his or her pool. If the cat *lost* all of his or her chips during a fight, then only healing will make him or her better (see Healing). However, if some of the cat's chips are missing because they were spent rather than lost, then those chips come back normally when the Narrator says it's time to refresh everyone's chips.

Losing Chips vs. Spending Chips

The number of chips you have will change frequently during the course of an adventure. Some you will spend on Ability and Skill Checks, others you'll spend to activate Knacks, and some you will lose as the result of damage. Although these may all seem alike, there is a very big difference between chips you spend and those you lose.

When you *spend* a chip, whether it's on a Check or a Knack, it gets set aside in one pile. This is the pile of chips that you will regain when the Narrator says it is time to refresh your chips.

When you *lose* a chip because your cat has taken damage, it gets put aside in a separate pile—preferably in a pouch or bag of some sort. This pile of chips can only be regained when your cat's wounds heal.

Healing

Suffering wounds is a serious problem because it greatly decreases the number of choices your character has during the game. Unfortunately, there are only a few ways to heal wounds.

In all but the worst cases, cats heal naturally over time. Every morning, a cat will heal 1 chip worth of wound damage. Take all the chips lost because of damage and randomly select one. Return that chip to your current Ability chip pool.

Fortunately, every Clan has at least one medicine cat with a collection of various remedies and herbs. If a wounded cat is in a Clan's camp or is somewhere that he or she has access to the correct healing herbs, once per day that cat may try to get extra healing from an Herb Lore or Medicine Lore Check (made by that cat, another player's cat, or the Clan medicine cat, whichever you prefer). If the result of this Check is lower than the number of chips the cat currently has lost because of wounds, no extra healing occurs. If the Check is equal to or higher than the number of chips currently lost, the cat heals 1 extra chip (as described above). If the Check is more than double the number of chips currently lost, the cat heals 2 extra chips.

Who Is the Narrator?

Over the last several chapters, these rules have occasionally referred to the "Narrator" as a player who is responsible for making various decisions during an adventure. But who is the Narrator?

You are—or, rather, sometimes you are.

Since the *Warriors Adventure Game* is a storytelling game, someone has to know the answers to the questions that will pop up about any particular scene, such as: How big is that tree? What can the cats see? What happens next?

However, since the Narrator knows all the answers and describes the situations that the cats must overcome, the person doing that job can't play a cat, too. And since the real fun of the game is playing a cat, the rules make it so that all the players take turns being the Narrator.

Anyone who has ever told a story to his or her friends—any kind of story, from a fairy tale to details of what happened at school last week—has the skills to be the Narrator for a little while. And some people may even find they like being the Narrator just as much as playing their cat characters.

Chapter by Chapter

So far we've talked about an adventure as a single story that the cats go through. But, just like a novel, an adventure has chapters.

You can think of being the Narrator as being the person reading out loud to the group so everyone can enjoy a story together. At the end of each chapter, you pass the book to the next person, who reads for a while. That way everyone gets chances to enjoy both telling the story and being surprised by what happens next.

The adventures for the *Warriors Adventure Game* are split up with natural breaking points that tell you to switch Narrators. So all the players get a chance to play their cats most of the time but also occasionally to tell the tale for a little while.

Details on what it means to be a Narrator can be found in Chapter Six, but it's really very straightforward.

Adventure Awaits

Once everyone is set, you can begin playing right away using "Saving the Kits," the mini-adventure in Chapter Eight.

When you're done with that, you can look for new, full-length adventures at the back of each book in the Warriors: Omen of the Stars series. You can also look for additional material on www.warriorcats.com.

Chapter Six: Advice for Narrators

One thing that makes the *Warriors Adventure Game* different from most other games you've probably played is the need for a Narrator. Stories, after all, must be told by someone. And if your cats are the heroes of the story, they can't very well dictate their own adventures. There would be no sense of surprise, mystery, or danger.

Then again, the thing that will bring most players to the *Warriors Adventure Game* is the chance to play their cats. So it would be a shame to make it so that every group had to choose one player who couldn't do that very thing.

For that reason, the players take turns being the Narrator throughout the course of an adventure. That way, no one is forced to give up his or her cat for more than a scene or two at a time, and everyone gets a chance to try his or her hand at being the Narrator (which can be an awful lot of fun, too).

How It Works

Every adventure in the *Warriors Adventure Game* is broken down into chapters, like in a book, and each chapter has a number of scenes in it. The adventure will clearly say where each chapter begins and ends, and each person only has to be the Narrator for one chapter at a time.

Before you start an adventure, your group must decide who will be the Narrator first. Pick a name out of a hat or do rock-paper-scissors or whatever method your group prefers, so long as it is fair, and figure out an order for people to be Narrator. The first person will set aside his or her cat for the moment, pick up the adventure, and read the first chapter.

Scenes

Each chapter in an adventure is made up of a series of scenes that describe actions, questions, and decision points. In each scene the Narrator reads a short passage aloud to the other players, telling them where their cats are and what is happening.

The scene will have further information for the Narrator, telling him or her in detail what is happening and giving other details, but what happens next is up to the players. Based on what the Narrator has read, the players decide what their cats want to do about it.

The Narrator's job is to answer the player's questions to help them better understand the situation and know what their cats' options are. Then when the players decide what their cats want to do, the Narrator uses the information written in the scene to tell them what happens next.

Sometimes what happens next will depend on the results of an Ability or Skill Check and at other times it will just be based on what the players have said, but the details will always be written clearly in the adventure. Each scene will end by telling the Narrator where to turn next and what to do.

When the scene brings an end to a chapter, the text will say that it is time for someone else to be the Narrator for a while. Pass the adventure to the next person and pick up your character sheet again.

Have Fun

The title "Narrator" sounds like an important one and, to be sure, the Narrator plays an important part in the *Warriors Adventure Game*. But there is no reason to be nervous about it. If you like telling stories or jokes or even just describing interesting things that happen during the day, then you're going to be a natural as a Narrator. The main thing you need to do is relax and have fun.

What Happens to the Narrator's Cat?

The player acting as the Narrator sets aside his or her cat. But where does that cat go?

The cat doesn't go anywhere. He or she is still with the group, just not doing anything active. This sort of thing happens all the time in books, movies, and TV shows. Scenes often focus on one or two characters while the others stay mostly in the background for a few minutes. That's what's going on here. A Narrator's cat is simply standing in the background while the other cats get to be the focus of the scene. When it's time to change Narrators, the focus will shift slightly and that cat will again become an active part of the adventure.

It's true that as the Narrator you will have to supervise the action for a scene. And it's also true that you may have to use your judgment to decide what the results of an Ability or Skill Check are. But if you follow the directions written in the scene and remember that everyone involved—from the players to the people who wrote the adventure—just wants you all to have fun, you'll be all right.

Be Fair

The first few times you play the *Warriors Adventure Game*, the toughest part about being the Narrator will probably be the times when a scene depends upon using the game rules in detail. This will be a new kind of game for most of the players (possibly including you), and the rules may sometimes seem a little overwhelming. If that happens, just remember this key rule:

Being fair and having fun is ALWAYS the right thing to do.

There is no rule in this booklet that is more important than that. If you are ever confused about the details of how a Knack or Skill works in a given situation, *always* choose the answer that seems the most fair.

Storytelling

The main job of the Narrator is to help move the story along. That begins with reading the scene descriptions, but it also includes other aspects. Let's take a look at the different things a Narrator is likely to have to do during a given scene.

Setting the Scene

Every scene starts with a bit of text the Narrator is supposed to read out loud to the players. In fact, there may be several bits of text like this that pop up as the scene progresses.

These bits of text give the players important information about what their cats see, smell, and feel. They're what the players use to try to figure out what to do next. Keep that in mind as you read these passages out loud.

If you have some skill at acting or can make interesting voices, by all means use that to enhance your reading. But remember that the most important thing is to be clear and informative. The most dramatic, emotional reading in the world won't be at all useful if it doesn't give the players the right idea of what's going on in the scene.

I Don't Want to Be the Narrator!

It is entirely possible that after trying it once or twice, you may find that you really don't like being the Narrator. That's okay. Some people just don't enjoy being the center of attention or having the responsibilities associated with telling the story.

You should try it once or twice before you make that decision, though. The Narrator's job sounds more complicated than it really is, and the adventure does most of the work for you.

If, after trying it a few times, you find that being the Narrator is something that you're just not suited for, talk about it with the other players. Chances are that one or more of them actually like that part of the game as much or more than playing their cats. You can make arrangements to trade responsibilities, or, if no one else wants to take an extra turn, you can just "pass" when your turn to be Narrator comes around.

Remember, this is a game and it's supposed to be fun. If being the Narrator stops you from enjoying yourself, then work with your friends and find a fair way to keep the game fun for everyone.

Let the Players Play

After reading the introductory text, the next thing the Narrator has to do is sit back and let the players decide what their cats want to do next. This sounds easy, but sometimes it can be harder than it seems.

It's tempting to try to guide the players into making the choices you want them to make. It can feel like the right thing to do because, after all, this is a storytelling game and you want to make sure the story turns out "right." But remember that there isn't a right or wrong way for the story to go. You have to allow the players and their cats to make their own decisions and, at times, make their own mistakes.

As long as the players understand the scene correctly, let them decide what to do on their own. Only jump in if it is clear that they are misunderstanding some part of what you've described to them.

Of course, if the players ask you for a clarification or your opinion or further description, then you should by all means give it. In fact, this leads to the next important job a Narrator has—making up stuff when the players ask about things that aren't written in the adventure.

Improvising

The adventures for the *Warriors Adventure Game* are written with an eye toward covering all the likely outcomes of any scene, and even to providing hints for what to do in the less likely cases. However, just as cats are forever curious and look in places they probably shouldn't, players will sometimes want to explore ideas for which the adventure is unprepared. At these times, it is the Narrator's job to improvise—to make up what happens and to help guide the players and the story back to one of the possibilities covered by the adventure.

This is probably the trickiest thing you will be asked to do as a Narrator, and while it takes a bit of quick thinking and creativity, it's not too difficult. The scenes will be described in enough detail so that you should be able, in your head, to answer the question "What would happen next if they did that?"

Getting the cats back on the right track might be a little more difficult. Once they start down a train of thought, players often like to stay on them until something more interesting comes along. So your best bet is to think of a way to make one of the options described in the scene seem more attractive to your friends.

If they just won't take a hint, though, there is nothing wrong with flat out telling them that the things they are doing are "off track" and letting them take a few steps back to try something else. Remember the main rule again—this is supposed to be fun. An adventure that meanders around with no rhyme or reason is frustrating for everyone—especially the Narrator.

Keep Everyone Involved

Every group of friends has some people who are more talkative than others, as well as individuals who tend to take the lead more often. This will almost certainly be true of the group of players in your game.

It's not really important that everyone gets equal time in a *Warriors Adventure Game* adventure, but it is important that no one feels left out. When it's your turn as the Narrator, you should try to make sure that everyone who wants to participate gets a chance, and even go so far as to encourage players who have been noticeably quiet. Give them chances to have the spotlight—they might like it.

Even when you're not the Narrator, you can keep an eye out for this sort of thing, and you can subtly help the Narrator by encouraging the quieter players to participate.

Avoid Splitting Up

One of the biggest potential problems in the *Warriors Adventure Game* is the possibility that some of the cats in the group will want to follow one path through the story while others will prefer a different route. In real life, it might be a good idea for the group to split in two and cover both possibilities, but this is not a good solution in terms of the game.

Splitting the group complicates matters by leading the players into two separate scenes and making it difficult (or sometimes impossible) for the Narrator to give everyone the proper information and attention. It also places an unfair burden on the Narrator, essentially doubling the amount of work and number of chapters he or she must oversee.

Unless the adventure specifically states that it is all right for the cats to split up into more than one group, the players should come to a single decision as to what the group will do at any juncture within a scene. Although the decision may be a difficult one, the actual choices at any juncture should always be clear. As Narrator, you may be called on to help the other players understand what their choices are, but you should not feel pressured into telling them more than their cats would reasonably be able to know—sometimes an adventure requires the heroes to make a decision and then live with the consequences.

As a player, you can help the Narrator by encouraging the other players to come to a consensus about what the cats should do next.

Ending the Chapter

When it's time to move on to the next chapter, the adventure will prompt you to pass the role of Narrator on to the next person. Often this will be at either a point of conclusion or a "cliffhanger." In either case, before you pass the adventure along to the next Narrator, you can help everyone stay focused and get a sense of dramatic completeness if you finish with some flair.

Describe the scene like the announcer at the end of a TV show that finishes with a big "to be continued!"

Use a tone of voice that invites the other players to ask you, "What comes next?" Then you can reply, "That's something the *next* Narrator will tell us!"

People often remember stories not because of what was in them, but because of how they were told. And it's always good to have a powerful ending.

Remember: it will eventually be your turn as Narrator again. If the players remember your scenes as being the most exciting, they will look forward to the next scene that you narrate.

Troubleshooting

No matter how thoroughly you know the rules or prepare for your turn as Narrator, there are still many little unexpected things that can crop up, causing confusion, stress, or worse for the players (including you). This is not a reflection on your skills as Narrator; these things are just sometimes part of any social activity such as the *Warriors Adventure Game*.

Below are tips for identifying and helping the group solve some of the most common problems.

Ask for Help

There's a lot to learn in these rules, and no one will know them all by heart. As the Narrator, you will often have information that the other players do not, making it difficult to get answers to any details that confuse you. Remember that you can always look through the rules to try to find solutions and, if your questions aren't answered, the basic rule is always to do what seems fair and fun.

It's possible that you'll run into a situation that just stumps you completely. Don't be afraid to ask for help, even if it spoils a little bit of the surprise for the other players. It's more important that everyone have a good time playing the game than it is that every moment of mystery or suspense be drawn out to its fullest. If you don't know a rule or can't figure out how to apply the ones you know to a certain situation, ask the other players. Together you may be able to find the answer or, if not, to arrive at a solution everyone agrees is fair and well suited for the adventure your cats are on.

Beware of Frustration

In just about every adventure, some scenes involve difficult tasks that may frustrate the players. Adventures are set up to be a little challenging, and that means presenting situations in which the characters can make bad decisions or have unpleasant things happen to them. This isn't the Narrator's fault, but you will be the one who has to deal with the consequences.

If you see players getting frustrated with the scene you are narrating, see if you can figure out what exactly is causing it. Are they confused about what is being asked of them or what their choices are? Are they unhappy because the choices they want to make are not given as options? Are the required Skill or Ability Checks too difficult (or too easy) for their cats?

If you can figure out what the problems are, then you can improvise steps to fix them. If the source of the frustration remains a mystery, stop the adventure and ask the players about it. Making sure everyone understands and is satisfied with how things are going will save time in the long run and make it more likely that the group as a whole will have fun.

It's Okay to Say "No"

When you're the Narrator, the players will be asking you lots of questions. In many cases they will want to do or try things that aren't covered in the adventure. As we said above, it's part of the Narrator's job to improvise in situations like that. It's also part of the Narrator's job to know when to say "no."

Sometimes players will suggest that their cats try truly ridiculous things. Often this is to set up an especially advantageous situation, but it just might be something they said because it seems funny at the time. There's nothing wrong with this. The players should talk about as many possible solutions as they want, even the ridiculous ones. But when it comes time to choose what the cats actually do, the players sometimes let the humor of the moment get the better of them. Inappropriate choices and behavior will only drag the game away from the adventure.

As the Narrator, you have the ability (and, in fact, the responsibility) to tell the players when the choices they're making are not in the spirit of the game. You shouldn't be rude or dismissive when you do this. After all, the players are probably just trying to have fun, which is the point of the game. However, the chances are that if only one or two players are making the inappropriate comments, the others are waiting for someone to take control; and when you're the Narrator that's something you should do.

But if everyone in the group is in the mood to goof around, then there are probably easier and more fun ways to do it than with these rules. It may be time to take a break from the game for a while.

Take a Break

Sometimes the problem will have less to do with what's going on in the story and more to do with what's happening at the table. If some of the players are tired or distracted or unhappy about something, it may become difficult for the group to focus on their cats and the problems unfolding in the scene.

At those times, a good solution is to suggest that the group take a break for a little while. Setting aside the game and dealing with whatever is occupying or bothering people is a much better idea than trying to sort real-world problems through the filter of fictional characters. The Narrator's job is not to solve everyone's problems for them, but it is to make sure that the game remains fun for the group as a whole.

Try It Again

Even if everyone tries his or her best, things can still go wrong. Sometimes the characters just make a series of poor choices that end up with an unpleasant result or an unhappy group. If this happens, remember that you can always try the scene over. In fact, if the group prefers, you can jump back several scenes or even whole chapters and explore an entirely different route through the story.

One of the best things about the *Warriors Adventure Game* is that you can have an unlimited number of "do overs." Of course, using these unnecessarily or at the first sign of any trouble will take away from the sense of danger and suspense that goes along with a good adventure; but if that's the way your group prefers to play the game, then you certainly can. As always, the operative rule is that the players have fun:

Chapter Seven: Cats of the Clans

The world of the Warriors novels is a rich and vibrant one, home to an ever-growing collection of cats your characters might want to meet and interact with. This chapter contains character sheets belonging to a handful of the cats you know from the novels, using the same Skills, Knacks, and other details that you have used to create your cats. These sheets are also available at www.warriorcats.com.

Think of these as examples for your cats. If they are true warriors and devote themselves to protecting their Clans and promoting the warrior code, they might grow to achieve these levels of experience—perhaps even more.

A Snapshot of the Heroes

The characters in the Warriors novels grow quickly. You can see them learning new things and improving on their abilities in every book, sometimes in almost every chapter. That makes it impossible for the character sheets in this chapter to stay 100 percent accurate. But that's really a chance for you to have some fun.

As new books come out and the characters learn and grow, think about the action the way a Narrator would in this game. Have the cats learned anything important? Has another moon passed for them to get improvements from? Is there something that they are doing that should be reflected on their character sheets? Then come back, look at these write-ups, and make additions. It might even be fun for you and your friends to do this together.

But there's more. These snapshots are of the cats at a certain point in time. But maybe you like them better the way they once were. Maybe you want a chance for your apprentice to meet Firestar when he was still just Firepaw. You can do that, too, though it's a little trickier.

The "Changes Over Time" chart in Chapter Four can act like a time machine. If you know what these characters are like here at a certain age, all you have to do is age them backwards—take off 5 or 6 moons, maybe more—and see how many Skills, Abilities, and Knacks they have to give up. Then make your own decisions about which specific ones they must lose. When you're done, you'll have a younger version of the cat—a snapshot of him or her from one of the earlier novels.

Cat's Name: Dovepaw

Player's Name: _____

Clan: ThunderClan

Cat's Color: Gray

Cat's Age: 6 _____ moons

Strength
2

Intelligence
1

Spirit
2

Skills

Arch (Strength)	**Jump** (Spirit)	**Smell** (Intelligence)
Bite (Strength)	**Listen** (Spirit)	**Sneak** (Spirit)
Climb (Strength)	**Ponder** (Intelligence) +1	**Swat** (Intelligence) +1
Focus (Spirit)	**Pounce** (Intelligence) +1	**Swim** (Strength)
Hiss (Spirit)	**See** (Intelligence) +1	**Wrestle** (Strength)

Knacks

Warriors Adventure Game created by Staal • www.storytimeswithstaal.com • Art by James L. Barry • www.jlbarry.com

Cat's Name: Lionblaze

Player's Name: _____

Clan: ThunderClan

Cat's Color: Golden Tabby

Cat's Age: 24 _____ moons

Strength	Intelligence	Spirit
6	3	2

Skills

Arch (Strength)	**Jump** (Spirit) +2	**Smell** (Intelligence)
Bite (Strength)	**Listen** (Spirit)	**Sneak** (Spirit)
Climb (Strength)	**Ponder** (Intelligence) +1	**Swat** (Intelligence) +2
Focus (Spirit)	**Pounce** (Intelligence) +1	**Swim** (Strength)
Hiss (Spirit)	**See** (Intelligence) +1	**Wrestle** (Strength) +2

Knacks

Belly Rake	
Leap	
Mighty Swat (x2)	
Pin	
Pummel	
Stalk	

HarperCollins*Children's Books*

Warriors Adventure Game created by Stuff • www.sleepingwolfdesign.com • Art by James L. Barry • www.jlbarry.com

Cat's Name: Jayfeather

Player's Name: _____

Clan: ThunderClan

Cat's Color: Gray Tabby

Cat's Age: 24 moons

Strength

2

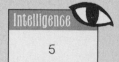

Intelligence

5

Spirit

4

Skills

Arch (Strength)	**Jump** (Spirit)	**Smell** (Intelligence) +1
Bite (Strength)	**Listen** (Spirit) +2	**Sneak** (Spirit) +1
Climb (Strength)	**Ponder** (Intelligence) +3	**Swat** (Intelligence)
Focus (Spirit) +2	**Pounce** (Intelligence)	**Swim** (Strength)
Hiss (Spirit)	**See** (Intelligence)	**Wrestle** (Strength)

Knacks

Alertness (x3)	
Clan Lore	
Herb Lore	
Interpret Dreams	
Medicine Lore	

Warriors Adventure Game created by Stan! • www.storytimeswithstan.com • Art by James L. Barry • www.jlbarry.com

WARRIORS ADVENTURE GAME

Cat's Name: Mistyfoot

Player's Name: _____

Clan: RiverClan

Cat's Color: Gray

Cat's Age: 36 moons

Strength

3

Intelligence

4

Spirit

4

Skills

Arch (Strength)	**Jump** (Spirit) +1	**Smell** (Intelligence) +1
Bite (Strength)	**Listen** (Spirit) +1	**Sneak** (Spirit)
Climb (Strength)	**Ponder** (Intelligence) +2	**Swat** (Intelligence) +2
Focus (Spirit) +2	**Pounce** (Intelligence)	**Swim** (Strength) +2
Hiss (Spirit)	**See** (Intelligence)	**Wrestle** (Strength)

Knacks

Alertness	
Balance	
Clan Lore (x2)	
Feint (x2)	
Orate (x2)	
Pathfinder	
Track	
Yowl	

Warriors Adventure Game created by Stan! • www.storygameswithstan.com • Art by James L. Barry • www.jlbarry.com

Cat's Name: _Tigerstar_

Player's Name: _____

Clan: _ShadowClan_

Cat's Color: _Tabby_

Cat's Age: _48_ moons

 Strength	 Intelligence	 Spirit
8	4	3

Skills

Arch (Strength)	**Jump** (Spirit)	**Smell** (Intelligence)
Bite (Strength) +3	**Listen** (Spirit)	**Sneak** (Spirit) +1
Climb (Strength)	**Ponder** (Intelligence) +1	**Swat** (Intelligence) +4
Focus (Spirit)	**Pounce** (Intelligence) +2	**Swim** (Strength)
Hiss (Spirit)	**See** (Intelligence)	**Wrestle** (Strength) +3

Knacks

Alertness (x2)	Stalk
Chomp	Track (x2)
Clan Lore	
Leap	
Mighty Swat (x2)	
Orate	
Pin	
Pummel (x2)	
Spring	

Warriors Adventure Game created by Stan! • www.storyinthewild.stan.com • Art by James L. Barry • www.jlbarry.com

WARRIORS ADVENTURE GAME

Cat's Name: Firestar

Player's Name: _____

Clan: ThunderClan

Cat's Color: Red

Cat's Age: 40 moons

Strength	Intelligence 	Spirit 
5	6	4

Skills

Arch (Strength)	Jump (Spirit)	Smell (Intelligence) +1
Bite (Strength)	Listen (Spirit) +1	Sneak (Spirit)
Climb (Strength) +1	Ponder (Intelligence) +2	Swat (Intelligence) +3
Focus (Spirit) +1	Pounce (Intelligence) +1	Swim (Strength)
Hiss (Spirit)	See (Intelligence)	Wrestle (Strength) +2

Knacks

Alertness	Twoleg Lore
Balance	
Clan Lore	
Dodge (x2)	
Feint	
Interpret Dreams	
Launch (x2)	
Pin (x2)	
Track	

www.warriorcats.com

HarperCollins*Children'sBooks*

Warriors Adventure Game created by Stані • www.shorylimewithian.com • Art by James L. Barry • www.jlbarry.com

Chapter Eight: Saving the Kits

"Saving the Kits" is a short sample adventure that will help you to get a feel for how the *Warriors Adventure Game* is played. Because this adventure is so brief, there are two parts of game play that will be slightly different than those described in the rules.

One Narrator

Despite what it says in Chapter Six about the Narrator switching from time to time during the course of an adventure, this does not happen during the course of "Saving the Kits." Because "Saving the Kits" is just a sample adventure—not much longer than a single "chapter" in a full-length adventure—switching Narrators in the middle of it would be confusing.

As a result, your group should choose one player to be the Narrator throughout this whole adventure. While it's unfortunate that one player will have to set aside his or her cat for this adventure, it's the best way for everyone to experience the game. Don't worry. The other cats won't gain any advantage over the one set aside, and all the players will learn something together.

Find a fair way to determine which of the players will be the Narrator for "Saving the Kits" (rock-paper-scissors, evens and odds, etc.). Once that's set, let him or her hold the adventure—no one but the Narrator should read beyond the point that says "The Adventure Begins."

No Reset

Another thing that won't happen while playing "Saving the Kits" is that the cats will not have an opportunity to refresh their Ability chips. They will have to play through this whole adventure with only the chips they have at the start of it, so players will have to be extra careful about when they spend their chips —once they're gone, there won't be any more for the rest of the adventure.

The Narrator's first duty is to explain this to the other players. Moreover, the Narrator might want to remind the players of this fact during the game if they seem to be spending their Ability chips too quickly. Then again, sometimes the best way to learn a difficult lesson is to get it wrong a few times.

When all is said and done, if the players figure out about the right speed with which to spend chips in "Saving the Kits," they will have the right idea for future adventures.

The Adventure Begins

Hello, Narrator! It's time to begin playing "Saving the Kits." Make sure everyone has his or her character sheet, the correct number of chips, a piece of paper, and a pencil. Since this is the first time you're playing, don't be afraid to stop, ask questions, or look things up.

When you're ready, begin with **1** below.

1. On the Island

Special Note: This section is only needed if the cats are from different Clans. It gives them a reason to work together. If all the cats are from the same Clan, you can skip this section and continue with **2**.

Read Aloud: "The adventure begins on the Island— where the Clans meet in peace for the monthly Gatherings. In hopes of forging closer ties between the Clans, each of the leaders has sent a group of young warriors here today. Your leaders have told you to be on your best behavior and to meet as many other young cats as you can."

Narrator Tips: The purpose of this section is for the players to introduce their cats to one another. Your job as the Narrator is to encourage them each to say a little bit about their cats and to begin to get into character.

If the players are doing this on their own, you can sit back and let them talk. Just make sure that all the players are participating.

If any of the players are left out or if the group doesn't feel comfortable jumping right into the game, try helping them by asking different players some of the following questions (or others that you think would be interesting).

- What does your cat look like?
- Where does your cat sit or stand? Why?

- What's the best thing about being in your Clan?
- Now that you're a warrior, what are you most looking forward to?
- Why do you think the leaders organized this meeting?

Let this go on for a few minutes until the players seem comfortable speaking for and about their characters. When that happens, or if the players seem anxious to move on, continue below.

Read Aloud: "Your conversations are interrupted as Firestar bounds across the fallen tree and addresses the whole group.

"'While you young warriors have been gathering,' he meows, 'a group of queens was introducing the different Clans' kits to one another. This may have been a mistake, though. A group of kits has gone missing!'" Continue with **2**.

2. Lost Kits

Special Note: If your group of players all have cats from the same Clan, then the next "Read Aloud" section is spoken by that Clan's leader. (You can find a list of the current Clan leaders on www.warriorcats.com in case you need it.) If they are from different Clans, the section is spoken by Onestar.

Read Aloud: "A group of kits has snuck away from the Queens that were watching them. Every available warrior has been sent out to look for them, but we need your help, too!"

Narrator Tips: Let the players' cats ask as many questions as they like about the disappearance, using the following paragraph for general information. As the Narrator, you can improvise anything that isn't specified below.

The group of kits had been playing together all morning. The queens had to yell at them several times for wandering away from the rest of the group while chasing butterflies. No one is sure how long the kits have been missing because the

queens were busy with another group that got tangled in a bramble of nettles. When it was time to go back to the nursery for afternoon naps, they noticed the kits were gone.

When the questioning is through, the Clan leader or Onestar tells the cats that their assignment is to check out two places in particular: a meadow next to the horseplace and an outcropping of rocks just beyond it.

Have the cats each make a Ponder Check. Anyone who gets a result of 4 or higher remembers one of the following facts—the more cats who succeed at the Check, the more information they'll get.

- There are a lot of butterflies in that meadow this time of year.
- There's been a strong wind blowing from the meadow toward the outcropping of rocks the past few days.
- It rained a lot yesterday, and that means the kits may have left tracks in the mud that can be followed.
- Many forest animals and prey like to gather in the meadow on sunny days like this.
- Last night's patrol reported that the recent rain has made the snakes that live in the outcropping of rocks more active and dangerous than usual.

What Happens Next: The group must decide where they are going to search first.

If the group wants to search the meadow first, continue with **3**.

If the group wants to search the rocks first, continue with **5**.

If the group wants to look for tracks, continue with **4**.

3. A Lovely Meadow

Read Aloud: "A beautiful open meadow stretches before you, dappled in sunlight and filled with long grass, flowers, and ferns. Above it all fly more butterflies than you can count, fluttering lazily in the breeze. It's all so peaceful you could almost forget the troubles that brought you here. It would be so nice to laze about in the sun."

Narrator Tips: First thing, have every character make a Focus Check with the following results.

- <u>Focus Check = 4 or Higher:</u> The cats whose checks were 4 or higher can continue about their business. When they notice the other cats are gone, they can call them back whenever they like. If they don't, the other cats can't participate in the adventure, so as the Narrator, you should remind them that it's important to keep the group together.

- <u>Focus Check = 3 or Lower:</u> The cats whose scores were 3 or lower are distracted by the warmth of the sun and the beauty of the meadow, and all they can think about is playing with the butterflies or lying in the sun. They are too distracted to continue and will stay here until someone reminds them of their mission. If *all* of the cats scored lower than 3, go immediately to the "What Happens Next" section.

Ask the players whose cats want to investigate the field how they plan to do so. Let them try to think of things to do rather than give them hints right away. They can use different Skills with the following results (plus any others that make sense to you). You don't have to do this in a strict order; just make sure everyone has a chance to try one thing before you let others try second or third options.

<u>Listen:</u> If the Check is 4 or higher, the cat hears some rustling in the grass on the far side of the meadow.

<u>Ponder:</u> If the Check is 3 or higher, the cat remembers that poppy seeds grow in one corner of the meadow —if the kits went there, they almost certainly have fallen deeply asleep. If the Check is 4 or higher, the cat also remembers that there's a section that's usually muddy after a rain, and that would be a good place to look for tracks.

<u>See:</u> If the Check is 3 or higher, the cat sees a set of paw prints leading to the far side of the meadow. If the Check is 4 or higher, the cat also sees a set of paw prints leading away toward the rocky outcropping. If the Check is 5 or higher, the cat realizes that the first set of prints do *not* belong to a kit but rather to some other woodland animal.

<u>Smell:</u> If the Check is 4 or higher, the cat smells something unpleasant on the far side of the meadow. If the Check is 5 or higher, the cat also smells a faint odor of poppy seeds coming from another corner of the meadow. If the Check is 6 or higher, the cat also catches a brief scent of the kits on a breeze blowing from the direction of the outcropping of rocks.

Let the players talk about what their cats discovered.

What Happens Next: What happens next depends on many different factors.

If *all* of the cats fail the initial Focus Check, continue with **6**.

If the group heads to the far side of the meadow, continue with **7**.

If the group goes to where the poppy seeds are, continue with **8**.

If the group goes toward the outcropping of rocks, continue with **5**.

4. Tracks

Read Aloud: "Thanks to yesterday's rain, the ground here is still fairly muddy. After only a few minutes of poking around, you are able to identify two distinct sets of paw prints."

Narrator Tips: One set of prints heads toward the outcropping of rocks; the other heads into the meadow. The first set belongs to one of the kits; the other belongs to the skunk, though the cats may not know this right away.

If the cats have already encountered the skunk (or otherwise figured out that it's there), they can automatically tell the paw prints apart. If not, then they'll have to use their hunter's instincts to tell them what the tracks in the mud mean. They'll do that by making some Skill Checks. The following Skills and Knacks will be most useful, but let the cats try anything their players can think of, as long as it seems likely to help.

<u>Animal Lore or Ponder:</u> Knowledge about other animals will help tell the difference between the tracks. An Animal Lore Check that totals 4 or higher or a Ponder Check that totals 5 or higher will let the cat know that the tracks that lead into the meadow were made by a skunk.

<u>See:</u> Simple observation will tell the cats something about the animals that made the two tracks. A Check that totals 4 or higher will reveal that the tracks leading into the meadow were made by something the size of a full-grown warrior, and even heavier. The paws that made those tracks clearly have very sharp claws. Plus the tracks heading toward the rocks were made by a smaller, lighter creature—just about the right size for a kit.

<u>Smell:</u> Sniffing around the area will provide information if the Check total is 5 or higher. In that case, the cat will smell a foul, bitter, unpleasant odor lingering in the tracks leading to the meadow. If the Smell Check is 6 or higher, the cat also catches a faint whiff of the kits in the tracks heading toward the rocks.

Track: Hunting Skill is very much involved in this section, so a cat with this Knack can choose to use it to help with either the See or Smell Checks (or any other check the Narrator thinks is appropriate).

What Happens Next:

If the group follows the tracks that lead toward the meadow, continue with 7.

If the group follows the tracks that lead toward the outcropping of rocks, continue with 5.

5. At the Rocks

Read Aloud: "As you come out from the woods you can see a cliff that is so tall and rocky it almost looks like it was built by some Twolegs. There are other hills around the territories like this, and you know that they're all dangerous. Rocks sometimes fall from the tops; snakes and biting insects live in the nooks and crannies. And even without that, the rocks never get enough sun to make them worth even taking a nap on."

Narrator Tips: A quick look around will tell the cats that the kits did wander this way—their paw prints are all over the place wherever there's mud or a puddle. But because there are so many paw prints, it's difficult to tell where the kits went. The cats will have to use some of their Skills to discover more.

Smell: It's possible for a cat to get some information from the scents in the air. If the Smell Check is 3 or higher, they can definitely smell the kits. If the Check is 4 or higher, they also smell some snakes. In both cases, the wind swirling around the cliff makes it impossible to tell exactly where the kits or the snakes are.

Listen: If a cat just Listens, he or she may hear the kits calling for help. If the Listen Check is 4 or higher, the cats hear the call but can't figure out why the cries sound so faint and faraway. If the Check totals 5 or higher, they realize that the kits must be in a cave somewhere along the rock wall. But the blowing wind makes it impossible to tell exactly which one.

See: Looking around, a cat might notice a few things. If the See Check is 3 or higher, the cats notice that along with the kits' paw prints, there are recent tracks made by snakes slithering over the mud. They also notice a butterfly flying in the strong breeze; it seems to be struggling against the wind, trying to fly back toward the meadow. If the Check is 4 or higher, the cats also notice a small cave entrance along the rock wall. If the Check is 5 or higher, they also notice a larger cave entrance a bit farther away and half hidden behind a tall rock.

Ponder: If a cat just wants to puzzle this out with his or her brain, a Ponder Check is in order. If the Check is 2 or higher, the cats know that these rocks are pretty boring and would not hold the kits' interest for long. If the Check is 3 or higher, the cats realize that the kits probably would have left here quickly unless there was a reason they couldn't. If the Check is 4 or higher, the cats know that if an animal attacked or some other danger arose, the kits would probably try to hide. If the Check is 5 or higher, the cats remember that there are usually caves in rock walls such as this.

Also allow the cats to try other Skills or Knacks if the players want (you can suggest some, if you think it will be helpful) and improvise results that seem appropriate.

What Happens Next:

If the group wants to follow the butterfly back toward the meadow, continue with 3.

If the group wants to keep poking around to find more clues, continue with 14.

If the group wants to examine the small cave entrance, continue with 9.

If the group wants to examine the large cave entrance, continue with 14.

6. Goof Off

Special Note: If the cats get sleepy because they chewed on poppy seed leaves, then adjust the "Read Aloud" section to indicate that Onestar has found the group sleeping rather than goofing off.

Read Aloud: "It's a beautiful day! You can chase butterflies or wrestle with each other or just lie in the sun. It all seems so perfect until you hear a stern voice calling out.

"'What are you doing?!'

"It's Onestar, and he doesn't look happy!"

Narrator Tips: Lead the players through a brief conversation with Onestar. He wants to know why they've shirked their responsibilities. Let them try to explain, or simply apologize if they prefer. There really is no good excuse for this, but sometimes this happens to young cats. Hopefully they will learn from the experience.

Firestar will be very disappointed in them and suggest that maybe they were promoted to warriors too soon. Thankfully, another group of warriors was able to save the kits in time. He will remind them that if they can't be counted on to help their Clan in a time of need, they're no better than kittypets.

What Happens Next: The adventure is over for the cats. They have failed in their assignment and will have to make up for their mistakes by doing extra hunting and patrolling for the next moon or more.

The cats do *not* get any Experience rewards for this adventure.

7. Skunk

Read Aloud: "As you get near the other end of the meadow, you see some rustling in the grass. Maybe that's the kits playing? But no—as you get closer, you can smell a bitter scent that tells you it isn't kits. It's a skunk!

"Before you can turn around to leave, the skunk senses your approach and charges forward through the grass toward you."

Narrator Tips: The next step in this section depends on what the players want their cats to do. Let them discuss it, but tell them that they have to make up their minds quickly. The biggest difficulty is that the whole group must decide on one course of action. The most likely options are described below.

Run Away: Fleeing is easy, but the skunk will try to spray the cats as they run. All the cats must make Jump Checks to avoid the spray. In order to succeed, a cat needs to get 3 or higher on the Check. If more than half of the cats fail the Check, then the whole group gets caught in the skunk's spray.

Try to Scare It: The cats can try to use their Arch or Hiss Skills to scare the skunk away. Have each cat make a Skill Check, then add up all the results of those Checks. If the total of all those numbers is 10 or higher, the skunk is scared away. If the total is less than that, the skunk tries to spray the cats. This works just as in the "Wait Too Long" option below.

Fight: If the cats decide they want to fight the skunk, the details go immediately to the "What Happens Next" section below.

Wait Too Long: If you think the players are taking too long making up their minds, give them a warning such as, "Make up your mind soon or the skunk is just going to attack." If they continue to take too long, the skunk just sprays at them. The cats must all make Jump Checks. In order to succeed, each cat must make a Check equal to 4 or higher. If half or more of the cats fail the Check, then the whole group is caught in the skunk's spray. If the group succeeds, it's the same as in the "Running Away" option.

What Happens Next: The next step in the adventure depends on the outcome of this section.

If the group gets caught in the skunk's spray, continue with **10**.

If the cats successfully run away or scare the skunk away, continue with **4**.

If the cats decide to fight with the skunk, continue with **11**.

8. Poppy Seeds

Read Aloud: "In a corner of the meadow you find the patch of poppy plants. The air is filled with their intoxicating smell, and if the kits were here they wouldn't be able to resist chewing on the seeds until they fell asleep. But there are no kits here. Still, those flowers smell so good, it's hard to resist."

Narrator Tips: This section is just a simple test of the cats' willpower. Have each cat make a Focus Check. If the Check is 2 or lower, that cat can't resist the temptation to chew on some poppy seeds. Doing so causes the cat to lose 1 Spirit chip.

If losing that chip costs the cat his or her last Spirit chip, then the cat falls asleep.

If a character is supposed to spend a Spirit chip but has no more Spirit chips left in his or her pool, then the cat has gotten sick from eating too many poppy seeds.

What Happens Next:

If any of the cats get sick, continue with **10**.

If half or more of the cats fall asleep, continue with **6**.

If less than half of the cats fall asleep, the other cats are able to wake them and the whole group can go on searching for the kits. Continue with **4**.

9. Kits

Read Aloud: "As you get near the small cave entrance, you can hear the kits clearly. They seem to be half crying and half whispering.

"When you get right up to the cave entrance, you can see that it's too small for you or the kits to fit through, but inside you can see the kits all standing on a ledge huddled together."

Narrator Tips: The point of this segment is for the cats to have a quick conversation with the kits, who will tell them the details of what happened and about the snakes. Remember that the scene will be more dramatic if you act out what the kits are saying rather than just telling the players the information blandly.

The details are that the kits snuck away from the group to chase butterflies. They wound up near the meadow when one of them, a frisky little tabby named Wanderkit convinced the others that hunting snakes would be more exciting than chasing butterflies.

It was exciting, but dangerous. The snakes chased the kits into this cave and might have killed them, but Wanderkit got everyone up onto a ledge where they could better defend themselves.

The snakes backed off, but keep returning and trying again, so the kits are trapped on the ledge. They look tired and almost certainly won't be able to defend themselves the next time the snakes return.

The kits can tell the cats that the main entrance to the cave is behind a tall rock. They can also tell them that the snakes are probably still guarding the entrance.

What Happens Next: If the cats decide to attack the snakes, continue with **14**.

If the cats want to do anything else, remind them that the next time the snakes come into the cave they will almost certainly kill the kits. If the cats do not attack the snakes, the kits will die and the cats will be in big trouble with the leaders of their Clans. If they still don't want to help right away, the adventure is over right now and the cats do *not* get any Experience rewards for this adventure. You can continue with a modified version of Firestar's lecture from **6**.

10. Sick

Special Note: The details of this section will be slightly different depending on whether the cats get here because of eating too many poppy seeds or from being caught in the skunk's spray. Keep those details in mind as you play through the details.

Read Aloud: "You open your eyes and find yourself back in the Clan camp. Lifting your head is more difficult than it usually is, and when you try, the whole world seems to spin around you.

"'Don't move,' you hear a familiar voice meow. 'You're not ready to get up just yet.'"

Narrator Tips: The voice comes from the Clan's medicine cat. Although this may be in different camps if the players' cats are from separate Clans, the conversations will be so similar that you can pretend they're all taking place together.

The medicine cat will tell the characters that other warriors brought them home in very sick condition. But with the quick application of some healing herbs, the medicine cat has fixed it so that they will all be fine after a little extra rest.

Depending on the details of how they got there, you may have the cats get a visit from their Clan leader to talk about the appropriate behavior for a warrior on a mission. There's no shame in retreating from or falling to a stronger opponent, but eating yourself sick is unacceptable. (This is based on whether you, as a Narrator, think this would be helpful for the players—it's a way to give them advice from a character in the game.)

What Happens Next: The adventure is over for the cats. Because of their illness, they were unable to accomplish the goal of rescuing the kits. Thankfully other warriors did.

The cats do *not* get any Experience rewards for this adventure.

11. Fight

Read Aloud: "The skunk digs in its claws and growls angrily at you. You can see how sharp its claws and teeth are, and you realize that there's a reason (other than just the smell) that the Clans don't hunt skunks as prey."

Narrator Tips: A fight with the skunk works just like any other fight, as described in Chapter Five.

The skunk has a Strength of 3. Every Round on its turn, it makes two Swat Checks—one each against two different cats (one Check for each of its front claws). The skunk's Swat Check always equals 5. If only one cat remains to fight, the skunk only makes one attack.

Cats must use their Swat Skill when fighting a skunk. It is not possible to Wrestle with or Bite a skunk because of its spray. When trying to avoid the cats' Swat attacks, the skunk's Jump Check always equals 4.

If the skunk takes 4 chips worth of damage, it will run away. The cats have won the fight.

If a cat decides that the fight is too tough, he or she can run away rather than make a Swat Check. Once a cat runs away, he or she cannot come back to rejoin the fight. If more than half of the cats choose to run away, then the whole group must run away together.

What Happens Next: The outcome of a fight can be brutal if it goes badly.

If any of the cats is Knocked Out, the whole group must get that character to a medicine cat as quickly as possible. Continue with 12.

If the cats win the fight, continue with 4.

If the cats want to run away, continue with the "Run Away" section in 7.

12. Hurt

Special Note: The details of this section will change based on how the cats got hurt. Use your imagination and improvise based on what has happened in the adventure so far.

Read Aloud: "When you open your eyes, you immediately feel the lingering pain from your wounds.

"'Don't move too much,' meows the familiar voice of your medicine cat. 'You've already shown how brave you are; now show me how smart you are by lying still for a few days while your body heals.'"

Narrator Tips: It's certainly possible that not all of the cats were injured. If only one character is Knocked Out, the whole group had to work together to get him or her back to camp, and so the whole group had to give up the search for the kits. Thankfully, another group found and rescued them.

Although the cats will all go back to their separate Clans, the rest of this scene will be pretty much the same in each case. For that reason, it's okay to take a shortcut and only play through it once, telling the players about any individual differences separately.

There is no shame in losing a fight. In fact, standing your ground and fighting to the end is the mark of true bravery. The Clan's leader and other members of the Clan will certainly be proud of the cats for acting like real warriors and will probably stop by to say so.

It will take a few days, or maybe even weeks, for the characters to fully heal. When they are better, though, they'll be warmly welcomed back to their duties.

What Happens Next: The adventure is over for the cats. They acted bravely but, in the end, did not have what it took to overcome the dangers they faced.

Although they can be proud of the bravery they showed, the cats do *not* get any Experience rewards for this adventure.

13. Well Done

Read Aloud: "After you defeat the snakes, the kits come bounding out of the cave. They're tired, hungry, and scared, but still safe and healthy.

"When you get back to the camp, the kits immediately begin telling tales about how big and strong and brave you all were. And it's true; you were. You saved the kits!"

Narrator Tips: All stories need an ending. This is your chance to have one of the Clan leaders tell the characters what a good job they did.

It's also a good opportunity for the players to have their cats ask any questions they might have about what happened or what could have happened. (If you plan to play this adventure again, though, you probably shouldn't give them too many answers.)

When that's done, so is the adventure.

What Happens Next: You have finished the adventure. Well done!

14. Snake Fight

Read Aloud: "Behind a tall rock you see a cave entrance. Slithering back and forth in front is a pair of vipers. They look angry and seem focused on something inside the cave—until they notice you!"

Narrator Tips: The fight with the snakes works just like any other fight, as described in Chapter Five. The only difficulty for the Narrator is that there are two snakes, so be sure to track each one separately (it's best to use a piece of scrap paper for this). Another complication is that the snakebites are poisonous.

Each snake has a Strength of 2. Every Round on their turn, the snakes will each attack one cat (if possible, the cat who hit it most recently). The snakes don't have Swat attacks, just Bites. These bites only do 1 point of damage if they hit (there is no extra damage as with cat Bites, as described in Chapter Five). However, they are poisonous.

A cat who has been bitten by a snake is poisoned and will remain that way until he or she gets treatment from a medicine cat. Every Round, the cat must make a Spirit Check. If that Check equals 3 or higher, nothing happens immediately. If the Check totals 2 or lower, the cat loses 1 chip (player's choice). Some cats have a high enough Spirit to pass this test easily, but it gets more difficult if the cat is bitten more than once. For every time a snake bites a cat, the difficulty of the Spirit Check goes up by 1. So if a cat is bitten twice, he or she loses a chip if the Spirit Check is 3 or lower. If the cat is bitten three times, he or she loses a chip if the Spirit Check is 4 or lower, and so on.

When the cats attack, the snakes have a Jump Check equal to 5. They are fast and hard to hit, but not very tough. Each snake can only take 3 points of damage and then it dies.

Also, if the fight goes on too long, the snakes will get discouraged and leave. After six Rounds of fighting, instead of attacking on their turn, the snakes turn around and run away. They slither under some large rocks and will not come out again until after the cats leave.

What Happens Next: Win or lose, this fight is the climax of the adventure.

If the cats kill or chase away the snakes, continue with 13, even if one or two of the cats were Knocked Out during the fight.

If *all* of the cats were Knocked Out during the fight, continue with 12.

After the Adventure

After the last scene of the adventure has been played, the game itself is not necessarily over. There are still a few things you can do if the players want to keep at it.

Play It Again

One of the great things about storytelling games is that you can always tell the story again. And, since so many of the events depend on Skill Checks, it won't always go exactly the same way.

There may be parts of the adventure that the cats never got around to exploring (especially if they went straight to the outcropping of rocks). Playing again will let everyone see all the parts of the story.

In particular, if the adventure ended badly, you and the players may want to try a second time, maybe starting back at the beginning or perhaps picking up somewhere in the middle where it feels as if things went wrong.

If you do play a second time, it's a good idea to let someone else try being the Narrator. That way, more people get that experience and the first Narrator gets to try playing the role of a cat.

Experience

If the cats completed the adventure successfully, then they all get Experience rewards (even the Narrator's cat). It is important to note, though, that each cat can only get experience from this adventure *once*! If you play through and successfully finish the adventure several times, your cat only gains the rewards listed below the *first* time he or she completes the adventure.

If you use different cats each time, though, each one can get the Experience rewards. The rule is *not* that a player can only get experience once; it's that a *cat* can.

Age: Although all the action in this adventure clearly happens in a single day, the presumption is that this is the most interesting and exciting thing that happens to your cat during the whole of that moon. Increase your cat's age by 1 moon and make any appropriate improvements described in Chapter Four.

Knack: On top of the improvements your cat gets from aging, he or she also learns a Knack. This can be a new Knack from the list in Chapter Three, or your cat can choose one of the Knacks he or she already has to get improved performance from it (if that's allowed in the Knack's description).

Rethinking Your Cat

Now that you've played once, it's time to think about how your cat worked in the game and whether or not it met your expectations. Look at the "Changing Your Cat" section in Chapter Four and think about what the best thing to do with your cat is. By the time you play another adventure or two, you should be very well acquainted with your cat, how he or she works under the game rules, and what improvements you'll want to make as you play the *Warriors Adventure Game* more often.

Have Fun

That's it! You've now finished your first adventure in the *Warriors Adventure Game*. We hope you enjoyed it and that you and your friends will want to play again.

More adventures can be found at the back of each novel in the Warriors: Omen of the Stars series, and you can find extra information at www.warriorcats.com.

Warriors Adventure Game created and written by Stan! • www.storytimewithstan.com
Art by James L. Barry • www.jlbarry.com

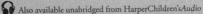